Kathryn Rich

A NEW WINDMILL COLLECTION OF PRE-1914
SHORT STORIES FOR GCSE PROSE STUDY

Generations

Edited by Mike Royston

Consultant: Lindsay McNab

Heinemann Educational Publishers
Halley Court, Jordan Hill, Oxford OX2 8EJ
Part of Harcourt Education

Heinemann is the registered trademark of
Harcourt Education Limited

Selection, introductions and activities © Mike Royston, 2003

First published 2003

07 06 05 04 03
10 9 8 7 6 5 4 3 2 1

British Library Cataloguing in Publication Data is available
from the British Library on request.

ISBN 0 435 12877 9

Acknowledgements
The publishers gratefully acknowledge the following for permission to reproduce
copyright material. Every effort has been made to contact copyright holders of material
reproduced in this book. Any omissions will be rectified in subsequent printings if notice
is given to the publishers.

p.15 The Random House Group Limited for an extract from *London: The Autobiography*
by Peter Ackroyd, published by Chatto and Windus; p.31 HMSO for Crown Copyright
material, reproduced under Class License Number C01W0000141 with the permission of
the Controller of HMSO and the Queen's Printer for Scotland; p.32 Princeton University
Press, USA for an extract from *Social and Economic Pressures: Feminism, Marriage and
the Law in Victorian England 1850-1895* by Mary Lydon Shanley © 1989 Mary Lydon
Shanley; pp.66-67 The Rural Development Commission for extracts from *The Village
Shop*, published by The Rural Development Commission, 1990; p.67 Elizabeth Hambro
and Sophie Gurney for an extract from *Period Piece* by Gwen Raverat, published by
Faber and Faber; pp.96-97 The Orion Publishing Group Limited for an extract from
Edward VII by Keith Middlemass, published by Weidenfeld and Nicholson; pp.104-105
Oxford University Press for an extract from *The Dictionary of Superstitions*, edited by
Iona Opie and Moria Tatem, 1993; p.145 Sutton/Haynes Publishing for an extract from
The Secret Life of Wilkie Collins by William M. Clark, published by Sutton Publishing;
p.146 Thomson Gale for an extract from *The Dream Encyclopedia* by James R. Lewis.
Copyright © 1995 Gale Research; p.146 W. Foulsham and Co. Limited for an extract from
Classic 1000 Dreams, published by Foulsham, 1991; p.147 Bookmart Limited for an
extract from *Encyclopedia of the Unexpected* by Reuben Stine, published by Bookmart,
1993; p.157 Oxford University Press, UK for an extract from *Oxford Reader's Companion
to Dickens*, edited by Paul Schlicke, published by Oxford University Press, 1999; p.157
Citadel Press/Kensington Publishing Corporation for an extract from *The Book of Spells*
by Stuart Gordon. Copyright © 1994 Stuart Gordon. All rights reserved.
www.kensingtonbooks.com; pp.168-169 Connexions for extracts from
www.connexions.co.uk; p.169 Rupert Matthews for an extract from *Haunted* by Rupert
Matthews, published by Ginn, 1997. Copyright © Rupert Matthews.

Cover design by Forepoint
Cover photo: Getty

Typeset by ⚈ Tek-Art, Croydon, Surrey
Printed and bound in the United Kingdom by Clays Ltd, St Ives Plc

Tel: 01865 888058 www.heinemann.co.uk

Contents

Introduction for students

This collection of stories will help you with your GCSE English/English Literature coursework, in particular the unit called Prose Study.

For Prose Study you have the option of reading a group of pre-1914 short stories. This book offers you a choice between two groups, or 'clusters', of stories. Those in Cluster 1 are linked by theme: *Within the Family.* Those in Cluster 2, *Strange and Supernatural*, are linked by genre. The stories are all by major writers who present their subjects in ways that will entertain you, stimulate your imagination and challenge you to think for yourself.

When you come to write about the stories, you have to do three things: (i) analyse their subject matter and style (ii) make comparisons between them, and (iii) show how they reflect the time in which they were written. The activities and assignments at the back of this book point you to exactly what the examiners require. They give plenty of opportunity for oral work, pair work and group work so that you can explore the texts *actively* instead of being just a note-taker.

After each story, there is a separate section containing non-fiction passages linked to the themes of the stories. These will give you an understanding of the social, cultural and historical contexts in which the authors were writing. You can use the extracts as a basis for further research via the Internet, CD-Roms and other sources of information.

I hope this collection helps you to do well in the Prose Study part of your coursework – and, just as important, to enjoy it.

Mike Royston

CLUSTER 1

Within the Family

The Poor Relation's Story
Charles Dickens

He was very reluctant to take precedence of so many respected members of the family, by beginning the round of stories they were to relate as they sat in a goodly circle by the Christmas fire; and he modestly suggested that it would be more correct if 'John our esteemed host' (whose health he begged to drink) would have the kindness to begin. For as to himself, he said, he was so little used to lead the way that really – But as they all cried out here, that he must begin, and agreed with one voice that he might, could, would, and should begin, he left off rubbing his hands, and took his legs from under his armchair, and did begin.

I have no doubt (said the poor relation) that I shall surprise the assembled members of our family, and particularly John our esteemed host to whom we are so much indebted for the great hospitality with which he has this day entertained us, by the confession that I am going to make. But, if you do me the honour to be surprised at anything that falls from a person so unimportant in the family as I am, I can only say that I shall be scrupulously accurate in all I relate.

I am not what I am supposed to be. I am quite another thing. Perhaps before I go further, I had better glance at what I *am* supposed to be.

It is supposed, unless I mistake – the assembled members of our family will correct me if I do, which is very likely (here the poor relation looked mildly about him for contradiction); that I am nobody's enemy but my own. That I never met with any particular success in anything. That I failed in business because I was unbusiness-like and **credulous** – in not being prepared for the interested designs of my partner. That I failed in love, because I was ridiculously trustful – in thinking it impossible that Christiana could deceive me. That I failed in my expectations from my uncle Chill, on account of not being as sharp as he could have wished in worldly matters. That, through life, I have been rather put upon and disappointed in a general way. That I am at present a bachelor of between fifty-nine and sixty years of age, living on a limited income in the form of a quarterly allowance, to which I see that John our esteemed host wishes me to make no further allusion.

The supposition as to my present pursuits and habits is the following effect.

I live in a lodging in the Clapham Road – a very clean back room, in a very respectable house – where I am expected not to be at home in the day-time, unless poorly; and which I usually leave in the morning at nine o'clock, on pretence of going to business. I take my breakfast – my roll and butter, and my half-pint of coffee – at the old-established coffee-shop near Westminster Bridge; and then I go into the City – I don't know why – and sit in the Garraway's Coffee House, and on 'Change, and walk about, and look into a few offices and counting-houses where some of my relations or acquaintance are so good as to tolerate me, and where I stand by the fire if the weather happens to be cold. I get through the day in this way until five o'clock, and then I dine: at a cost, on the average, of one and threepence. Having still a little money to spend on my evening's entertainment, I look into the old-established coffee-shop as I go home, and take my cup of tea, and perhaps my bit of toast. So, as the large hand of the clock makes its way round to the morning hours again, I make my way round to the Clapham Road again, and go to bed when I get to my lodging – fire being expensive, and being objected to by the family on account of its giving trouble and making a dirt.

---

credulous: too trusting

Sometimes, one of my relations or acquaintance is so obliging as to ask me to dinner. Those are holiday occasions, and then I generally walk in the Park. I am a solitary man, and seldom walk with anybody. Not that I am avoided because I am shabby; for I am not at all shabby, having always a good suit of black on (or rather Oxford mixture, which has the appearance of black and wears much better); but I have got into a habit of speaking low, and being rather silent, and my spirits are not high, and I am **sensible** that I am not an attractive companion.

The only exception to this general rule is the child of my first cousin, Little Frank. I have a particular affection for that child, and he takes very kindly to me. He is a **diffident** boy by nature; and in a crowd he is soon run over, as I may say, and forgotten. He and I, however, get on exceedingly well. I have a fancy that the poor child will in time succeed to my peculiar position of the family. We talk but little; still, we understand each other. We walk about, hand in hand; and without much speaking he knows what I mean, and I know what he means. When he was very little indeed, I used to take him to the windows of the toy-shops, and show him the toys inside. It is surprising how soon he found out that I would have made him a great many presents if I had been in circumstances to do it.

Little Frank and I go and look at the outside of the Monument – he is very fond of the Monument – and at the Bridges, and at all the sights that are free. On two of my birthdays, we have dined on **à-la-mode** beef, and gone at half-price to the play, and been deeply interested. I was once walking with him in Lombard Street, which we often visit on account of my having mentioned to him that there are great riches there – he is very fond of Lombard Street – when a gentleman said to me as he passed by, 'Sir, your little son has dropped his glove.' I assure you, if you will excuse my remarking on so trivial a circumstance, this accidental mention of the child as mine, quite touched my heart and brought the foolish tears into my eyes.

---

sensible: aware
diffident: shy, retiring
à-la-mode: in fashion, costly

When Little Frank is sent to school in the country, I shall be very much at a loss what to do with myself, but I have the intention of walking down there once a month and seeing him on a half-holiday. I am told he will then be at play upon the Heath; and if my visits should be objected to, as unsettling the child, I can see him from a distance without his seeing me, and walk back again. His mother comes of a highly genteel family, and rather disapproves, I am aware, of our being too much together. I know that I am not calculated to improve his retiring disposition; but I think he would miss me beyond the feeling of the moment if we were wholly separated.

When I die in the Clapham Road, I shall not leave much more in this world than I shall take out of it; but, I happen to have a **miniature** of a bright-faced boy, with a curling head, and an open shirt-frill waving down his bosom (my mother had it taken for me, but I can't believe that it was ever like), which will be worth nothing to sell, and which I shall beg may be given to Frank. I have written my dear boy a little letter with it, in which I have told him that I felt very sorry to part from him, though bound to confess that I knew no reason why I should remain here. I have given him some short advice, the best of my power, to take warning of the consequences of being nobody's enemy but his own; and I have endeavoured to comfort him for what I fear he will consider a bereavement, by pointing out to him, that I was only a **superfluous** something to every one but him; and that having by some means failed to find a place in this great assembly, I am better out of it.

Such (said the poor relation, clearing his throat and beginning to speak a little louder) is the general impression about me. Now, it is a remarkable circumstance which forms the aim and purpose of my story, that this is all wrong. This is not my life, and these are not my habits. I do not even live in Clapham Road. Comparatively speaking, I am very seldom there. I reside, mostly, in a – I am almost ashamed to say the word, it sounds so full of pretension – in a Castle. I do not mean

---

miniature: small picture
superfluous: unimportant

that it is an old baronial habitation, but still it is a building always known to every one by the name of a Castle. In it, I preserve the particulars of my history; they run thus:

It was when I first took John Spatter (who had been my clerk) into partnership, and when I was still a young man of not more than five-and-twenty, residing in the house of my uncle Chill, from whom I had considerable expectations, that I ventured to propose to Christiana. I had loved Christiana a long time. She was very beautiful, and very winning in all respects. I rather mistrusted her widowed mother, who I feared was of a plotting and **mercenary** turn of mind; but, I thought as well of her as I could, for Christiana's sake. I never had loved any one but Christiana, and she had been all the world, and O far more than all the world, to me, from our childhood!

Christiana accepted me with her mother's consent, and I was rendered very happy indeed. My life at uncle Chill's was of a spare dull kind, and my **garret** chamber was as dull, and bare, and cold, as an upper prison room in some stern northern fortress. But, having Christiana's love, I wanted nothing upon earth. I would not have changed my lot with any human being.

Avarice was, unhappily, my uncle Chill's master-vice. Though he was rich, he pinched, and scraped, and clutched, and lived miserably. As Christiana had no fortune, I was for some time a little fearful of confessing our engagement to him; but, at length I wrote him a letter, saying how it all truly was. I put it into his hand one night, on going to bed.

As I came downstairs next morning, shivering in the cold December air; colder in my uncle's unwarmed house than in the street, where the winter sun did sometimes shine, and which was at all events enlivened by cheerful faces and voices passing along; I carried a heavy heart towards the long, low breakfast-room in which my uncle sat. It was a large room with a small fire, and there was a great bay window in it which the rain had marked in the night as if with the tears of houseless people. It stared upon a raw yard, with a cracked stone

---

mercenary: obsessed by money
garret: attic

pavement, and some rusted iron railings half uprooted, whence an ugly out-building that had once been a dissecting-room (in the time of the great surgeon who had mortgaged the house to my uncle), stared at it.

We rose so early always, that at that time of the year we breakfasted by candle-light. When I went into the room, my uncle was so **contracted** by the cold, and so huddled together in his chair behind the one dim candle, that I did not see him until I was close to the table.

As I held out my hand to him, he caught up his stick (being infirm, he always walked about the house with a stick), and made a blow at me, and said, 'You fool!'

'Uncle,' I returned, 'I didn't expect you to be so angry as this.' Nor had I expected it, though he was a hard and angry old man.

'You didn't expect!' said he; 'when did you ever expect? When did you ever calculate, or look forward, you contemptible dog?'

'These are hard words, uncle!'

'Hard words? Feathers, to pelt such an idiot as you with,' said he. 'Here! Betsy Snap! Look at him!'

Betsy Snap was a withered, hard-favoured, yellow old woman – our only **domestic** – always employed, at this time of the morning, in rubbing my uncle's legs. As my uncle adjured her to look at me, he put his lean grip on the crown of her head, she kneeling beside him, and turned her face towards me. An involuntary thought connecting them both with the Dissecting Room, as it must often have been in the surgeon's time, passed across my mind in the midst of my anxiety.

'Look at the snivelling milksop!' said my uncle. 'Look at the baby! This is the gentleman who, people say, is nobody's enemy but his own. This is the gentleman who can't say no. This is the gentleman who was making such large profits in his business that he must needs take a partner, t'other day. This is the gentleman who is going to marry a wife without a penny, and who falls into the hands of **Jezebels** who are speculating on my death!'

---

contracted: hunched-up
domestic: servant
Jezebels: two-faced schemers

I knew, now, how great my uncle's rage was; for nothing short of his being almost beside himself would have induced him to utter that concluding word, which he held in such repugnance that it was never spoken or hinted at before him on any account.

'On my death,' he repeated, as if he were defying me by defying his own **abhorrence** of the word. 'On my death – death – Death! But I'll spoil the speculation. Eat your last under this roof, you feeble wretch, and may it choke you!'

You may suppose that I had not much appetite for the breakfast to which I was bidden in these terms; but, I took my accustomed seat. I saw that I was repudiated henceforth by my uncle; still I could bear that very well, possessing Christiana's heart.

He emptied his basin of bread and milk as usual, only that he took it on his knees with his chair turned away from the table where I sat. When he had done, he carefully snuffed out the candle; and the cold, slate-coloured, miserable day looked in upon us.

'Now, Mr Michael,' said he, 'before we part, I should like to have a word with these ladies in your presence.'

'As you will, Sir,' I returned; 'but you deceive yourself, and wrong us, cruelly, if you suppose that there is any feeling at stake in this contract but pure, disinterested, faithful love.'

To this, he only replied, 'You lie!' and not one other word.

We went, through half-thawed snow and half-frozen rain, to the house where Christiana and her mother lived. My uncle knew them very well. They were sitting at their breakfast, and were surprised to see us at that hour.

'Your servant, ma'am,' said my uncle to the mother. 'You **divine** the purpose of my visit, I dare say, ma'am. I understand there is a world of pure, disinterested, faithful love cooped up here. I am happy to bring it all it wants, to make it complete. I bring you your son-in-law, ma'am – and you, your husband,

---

abhorrence: hatred
divine: guess

miss. The gentleman is a perfect stranger to me, but I wish him joy of his wise bargain.'

He snarled at me as he went out, and I never saw him again.

It is altogether a mistake (continued the poor relation) to suppose that my dear Christiana, over-persuaded and influenced by her mother, married a rich man, the dirt from whose carriage-wheels is often, in these changed times, thrown upon me as she rides by. No, no. She married me.

The way we came to be married rather sooner than we intended, was this. I took a **frugal** lodging and was saving and planning for her sake, when, one day, she spoke to me with great earnestness, and said:

'My dear Michael, I have given you my heart. I have said that I loved you, and I have pledged myself to be your wife. I am as much yours through all changes of good and evil as if we had been married on the day when such words passed between us. I know you well, and know that if we should be separated and our union broke off, your whole life would be shadowed, and all that might, even now, be stronger in your character for the conflict with the world would then be weakened to the shadow of what it is!'

'God help me, Christiana!' said I. 'You speak the truth.'

'Michael!' said she, putting her hand in mine, in all maidenly devotion, 'let us keep apart no longer. It is but for me to say that I can live contented upon such means as you have, and I well know you are happy. I say so from my heart. Strive no more alone; let us strive together. My dear Michael, it is not right that I should keep secret from you what you do not suspect, but what distresses my whole life. My mother: without considering that what you have lost, you have lost for me, and on the assurance of my faith: sets her heart on riches, and urges another **suit** upon me, to my misery. I cannot bear this, for to bear it is to be untrue to you. I would rather share your struggles than look on. I want no better home than you can

frugal: cheap
suit: marriage

give me. I know that you will aspire and labour with a higher courage if I am wholly yours, and let it be so when you will!'

I was blest indeed, that day, and a new world opened to me. We were married in a very little while, and I took my wife to our happy home. That was the beginning of the residence I have spoken of; the Castle we have ever since inhabited together, dates from that time. All our children have been born in it. Our first child – now married – was a little girl, whom we called Christiana. Her son is so like Little Frank, that I hardly know which is which.

* * *

The current impression as to my partner's dealings with me is also quite **erroneous**. He did not begin to treat me coldly, as a poor simpleton, when my uncle and I so fatally quarrelled; nor did he afterwards gradually possess himself of our business and edge me out. On the contrary, he behaved to me with the utmost good faith and honour.

Matters between us took this turn:— On the day of my separation from my uncle, and even before the arrival at our counting-house of my trunks (which he sent after me, *not* carriage paid), I went down to our room of business, on our little wharf, overlooking the river; and there I told John Spatter what had happened. John did not say, in reply, that rich old relatives were **palpable** facts, and that love and sentiment were moonshine and fiction. He addressed me thus:

'Michael,' said John, 'we were at school together, and I generally had the knack of getting on better than you, and making a higher reputation.'

'You had, John,' I returned.

'Although,' said John, 'I borrowed your books and lost them; borrowed your pocket-money, and never repaid it; got you to buy my damaged knives at a higher price than I had given for them new; and to **own** to the windows that I had broken.'

---

erroneous: wrong, mistaken
palpable: unavoidable
own: admit

'All not worth mentioning, John Spatter,' said I, 'but certainly true.'

'When you were first established in this infant business, which promises to thrive so well,' pursued John, 'I came to you, in my search for almost any employment, and you made me your clerk.'

'Still not worth mentioning, my dear John Spatter,' said I; 'still, equally true.'

'And finding that I had a good head for business, and that I was really useful *to* the business, you did not like to retain me in that capacity, and thought it an act of justice soon to make me your partner.'

'Still less worth mentioning than any of those other little circumstances you have recalled, John Spatter,' said I; 'for I was, and am, sensible of your merits and my deficiencies.'

'Now, my good friend,' said John, drawing my arm through his, as he had had a habit of doing at school; while two vessels outside the windows of our counting-house – which were shaped like the stern windows of a ship – went lightly down the river with the tide, as John and I might then be sailing away in company, and in trust and confidence, on our voyage of life; 'let there, under these friendly circumstances, be a right understanding between us. You are too **easy**, Michael. You are nobody's enemy but your own. If I were to give you that damaging character among our connexion, with a shrug, and a shake of the head, and a sigh; and if I were further to abuse the trust you place in me –'

'But you never will abuse it at all, John,' I observed.

'Never!' said he: 'but I am putting a case – I say, and if I were further to abuse that trust by keeping this piece of our common affairs in the dark, and this other piece in the light, and again this other piece in the twilight, and so on, I should strengthen my strength, and weaken your weakness, day by day, until at last I found myself on the high road to fortune, and you left behind on some bare common, a hopeless number of miles out of the way.'

'Exactly so,' said I.

---

easy: easy-going

'To prevent this, Michael,' said John Spatter, 'or the remotest chance of this, there must be perfect openness between us. Nothing must be concealed, and we must have but one interest.'

'My dear John Spatter,' I assured him, 'that is precisely what I mean.'

'And when you are too easy,' pursued John, his face glowing with friendship, 'you must allow me to prevent that imperfection in your nature from being taken advantage of, by any one; you must not expect me to humour it –'

'My dear John Spatter,' I interrupted, 'I *don't* expect you to humour it. I want to correct it.'

'And I, too,' said John.

'Exactly so!' cried I. 'We both have the same end in view; and, honourably seeking it, and fully trusting one another, and having but one interest, ours will be a prosperous and happy partnership.'

'I am sure of it!' returned John Spatter. And we shook hands most affectionately.

I took John home to my Castle, and we had a very happy day. Our partnership throve well. My friend and partner supplied what I wanted, as I had foreseen that he would; and by improving both the business and myself, amply acknowledged any little rise in life to which I had helped him.

I am not (said the poor relation, looking at the fire as he slowly rubbed his hands) very rich, for I never cared to be that; but I have enough, and am above all moderate wants and anxieties. My Castle is not a splendid place, but it is very comfortable, and it has a warm and cheerful air, and is quite a picture of Home.

Our eldest girl, who is very like her mother, married John Spatter's eldest son. Our two families are closely united in other ties of attachment. It is very pleasant of an evening, when we are all assembled together – which frequently happens – and when John and I talk over old times, and the one interest there has always been between us.

I really do not know, in my Castle, what loneliness is. Some of our children or grandchildren are always about it, and the young voices of my descendants are delightful – O, how delightful! – to me to hear. My dearest and most devoted wife, ever faithful, ever loving, ever helpful and sustaining and consoling, is the priceless blessing of my house; from whom all its other blessings spring. We are rather a musical family, and when Christiana sees me, at any time, a little weary or depressed, she steals to the piano and sings a gentle air she used to sing when we were first betrothed. So weak a man am I, that I cannot bear to hear it from any other source. They played it once, at the Theatre, when I was there with Little Frank; and the child said wondering, 'Cousin Michael, whose hot tears are these that have fallen on my hand?'

Such is my Castle, and such are the real particulars of my life therein preserved. I often take Little Frank home there. He is very welcome to my grandchildren, and they play together. At this time of year – the Christmas and New Year time – I am seldom out of my Castle. For, the associations of the season seem to hold me there, and the **precepts of the season** seem to teach me that it is well to be there.

'And the Castle is –' observed a grave, kind voice among the company.

'Yes. My Castle,' said the poor relation, shaking his head as he still looked at the fire, 'is in the Air. John our esteemed host suggests its situation accurately. My Castle is in the Air! I have done. Will you be so good as to pass the story!'

---

precepts of the season: rules or requirements of Christmas

Non-fiction passages linked to
The Poor Relation's Story (1852)

Poverty in London during the 1850s

a On the street in a fashionable area of London near Covent Garden:

> A hundred foul lanes and alleys have debauched, on to the spick-and-span new promenade, unheard of human horrors. Gibbering forms of old men and women in filthy rags, with fiery heads of shock hair, the roots beginning an inch from the eyebrows, with the eyes themselves bleared and gummy, with gashes filled with yellow fangs for teeth, with rough holes punched in the nasal cartilage for nostrils … awful deformities, with horrifying malformations of the limbs and running sores.

Thomas Beames, 1850

b An American tourist saw rich and poor living side by side:

> In the midst of the most extraordinary abundance, here are men, women and children dying of starvation; and running alongside of the splendid chariot, with its gilded equipages, its silken linings and its liveried footmen, are poor, forlorn, friendless, almost naked wretches, looking like the mere fragments of humanity.

Henry Colman, 1840

c Families sometimes sold their children to be chimney-sweeps:

The chimney-sweeps, apprentices known as 'climbing boys', were usually attached to their masters at the age of seven or eight, although it was also common for impoverished parents to sell children as young as four years old for twenty or thirty shillings. Small size was important, because the flues of London houses were characteristically narrow and twisted so that they became easily choked with soot or otherwise constricted. The young climbing boys were prodded or pushed into these tiny spaces, then sometimes pricked with pins or scorched with fire to make them climb more readily. Some died of suffocation. Others grew deformed. A social reformer described a typical climbing boy at the close of his short career. 'He is now twelve years of age, a cripple on crutches, hardly three feet seven inches in stature. His hair felt like a hog's bristle, and his head like a warm cinder. He repeats the Lord's Prayer.' These children, blackened by the soot and refuse of the city, were rarely, if ever, washed.

Peter Ackroyd, 2000

d Some of London's poor searched the sewers to make a living:

> 'Bless your heart, the smell's nothink,' said the man who searched in the sewers for anything saleable, 'it's a roughish smell at first, but nothink near so bad as you thinks, 'cause, you see, there's sich lots o'water always a-comin down the sewer … The rats is wery dangerous, that's sartin, but we always go three or four on us together, and the varmint's too wide awake to tackle us then, for they know they'd git off second best … The reason I likes this sort of life is 'cause I can sit down when I likes, and nobody can't order me about. When I'm hard up, I knows as how I must work, and then I goes at it like sticks a-breaking; and tho' the times isn't as they was, I can go now and pick up my four or five bob a day, where another wouldn't know how to get a brass farden.'

Henry Mayhew, 1852

e Like the Poor Relation, many Londoners living in poverty had come down in the world:

> 'I lodge in Charles Street, Drury Lane, now. I did live in Nottingham Court once and Earl Street. But, Lord, I've lived in many places you wouldn't think, and I don't imagine you'd believe one half. You folksas has honour, and character, and feelings, and such, can't understand how all that's been beaten out of people like me. I don't feel it. I'm used to it. I don't suppose I'll live much longer, and that's another thing that pleases me. I don't want to live, and yet I don't care enough about dying to make away with myself. I aren't got that amount of feeling that some has, and that's where it is.'

Henry Mayhew, 1856

The Half-Brothers
Elizabeth Gaskell

My mother was twice married. She never spoke of her first husband, and it is only from other people that I have learnt what little I know about him. I believe she was scarcely seventeen when she was married to him; and he was barely one-and-twenty. He rented a small farm up in Cumberland, somewhere towards the sea-coast; but he was perhaps too young and inexperienced to have the charge of land and cattle: anyhow, his affairs did not prosper, and he fell into ill health, and died of consumption before they had been three years man and wife, leaving my mother a young widow of twenty, with a little child only just able to walk, and the farm on her hands for four years more by the lease, with half the stock on it dead, or sold off one by one to pay the more pressing debts, and with no money to purchase more, or even to buy the provisions needed for the small consumption of every day.

There was another child coming, too; and sad and sorry, I believe, she was to think of it. A dreary winter she must have had in her lonesome dwelling, with never another near it for miles around; her sister came to bear her company, and they two planned and plotted how to make every penny they could raise go as far as possible.

I can't tell you how it happened that my little sister, whom I never saw, come to sicken and die; but, as if my poor mother's cup was not full enough, only a fortnight before Gregory was born the little girl took ill of scarlet fever, and in a week she lay dead. My mother was, I believe, just stunned with this last blow. My aunt has told me that she did not cry; aunt Fanny would have been thankful if she had; but she sat holding the poor wee lassie's hand, and looking in her pretty, pale, dead face, without so much as shedding a tear. And it was all the same, when they had to take her away to be buried. She just kissed the child, and sat her down in the window-seat to watch the little black train of people (neighbours, my aunt, and one far-off cousin, who were all the friends they could muster) go winding away amongst the snow, which had fallen thinly over the country the night before.

When my aunt came back from the funeral, she found my mother in the same place, and as dry-eyed as ever. So she continued until after Gregory was born; and, somehow, his coming seemed to loosen the tears, and she cried day and night, day and night, till my aunt and the other watcher looked at each other in dismay, and would **fain** have stopped her if they had but known how. But she bade them let her alone, and not be over-anxious, for every drop she shed eased her brain, which had been in a terrible state before for want of the power to cry. She seemed after that to think of nothing but her new little baby; she hardly appeared to remember either her husband or her little daughter that lay dead in Brigham churchyard – at least so aunt Fanny said; but she was a great talker, and my mother was very silent by nature, and I think aunt Fanny may have been mistaken in believing that my mother never thought of her husband and child just because she never spoke about them.

Aunt Fanny was older than my mother, and had a way of treating her like a child; but, for all that, she was a kind, warm-hearted creature, who thought more of her sister's welfare than she did of her own; and it was on her bit of money that they principally lived, and on what the two could earn by working for the great **Glasgow sewing-merchants**. But by-and-by my mother's eyesight began to fail. It was not that she was exactly blind, for she could see well enough to guide herself about the house, and to do a good deal of domestic work; but she could no longer do fine sewing and earn money. It must have been with the heavy crying she had had in her day, for she was but a young creature at this time, and as pretty a young woman, I have heard people say, as any on the country side. She took it sadly to heart that she could no longer **gain**

---

fain: gladly
Glasgow sewing-merchants: the sisters are 'out-workers' employed at home
gain: contribute

anything towards the keep of herself and her child. My aunt Fanny would fain have persuaded her that she had enough to do in managing their cottage and minding Gregory; but my mother knew that they were **pinched**, and that aunt Fanny herself had not as much to eat, even of the commonest kind of food, as she could have done with; and as for Gregory, he was not a strong lad, and needed, not more food – for he always had enough, whoever went short – but better nourishment, and more flesh-meat.

One day – it was aunt Fanny who told me all this about my poor mother, long after her death – as the sisters were sitting together, aunt Fanny working, and my mother hushing Gregory to sleep, William Preston, who was afterwards my father, came in. He was reckoned an old bachelor; I suppose he was long past forty, and he was one of the wealthiest farmers thereabouts, and had known my grandfather well, and my mother and my aunt in their more prosperous days. He sat down, and began to twirl his hat by way of being agreeable; my aunt Fanny talked, and he listened and looked at my mother. But he said very little, either on that visit, or on many another that he paid before he spoke out what had been the real purpose of his calling so often all along, and from the very first time he came to their house.

One Sunday, however, my aunt Fanny stayed away from church, and took care of the child, and my mother went alone. When she came back, she ran straight upstairs, without going into the kitchen to look at Gregory or speak any word to her sister, and aunt Fanny heard her cry as if her heart was breaking; so she went up and scolded her right well through the bolted door, till at last she got her to open it. And then she threw herself on my aunt's neck, and told her that William Preston had asked her to marry him, and had promised to take good charge of her boy, and to let him want for nothing, neither in the way of keep nor of education, and that she had **consented**.

Aunt Fanny was a good deal shocked at this; for as I have said, she had often thought that my mother had forgotten her

pinched: hard up
consented: agreed to marry

first husband very quickly, and now here was proof positive of it, if she could so soon think of marrying again. Besides, as aunt Fanny used to say, she herself would have been a far more suitable match for a man of William Preston's age than Helen, who, though she was a widow, had not seen her four-and-twentieth summer. However, as aunt Fanny said, they had not asked her advice; and there was much to be said on the other side of the question. Helen's eyesight would never be good for much again, and as William Preston's wife she would never need to do anything, if she chose to sit with her hands before her; and a boy was a great charge to a widowed mother; and now there would be a decent, steady man to see after him. So, by-and-by, aunt Fanny seemed to take a brighter view of the marriage than did my mother herself, who hardly ever looked up, and never smiled after the day when she promised William Preston to be his wife. But much as she loved Gregory before, she seemed to love him more now. She was continually talking to him when they were alone, though he was far too young to understand her moaning words, or give her any comfort, except by his caresses.

At last William Preston and she were wed; and she went to be mistress of a well-stocked house, not above half an hour's walk from where aunt Fanny lived. I believe she did all that she could to please my father; and a more dutiful wife, I have heard him himself say, could never have been. But she did not love him, and he soon found it out. She loved Gregory, and she did not love him. Perhaps, love would have come in time, if he had been patient enough to wait; but it just turned him sour to see how her eye brightened and her colour came at the sight of that little child, while for him who had given her so much, she had only gentle words as cold as ice.

He got to **taunt** her with the difference in her manner, as if that would bring love; and he took a positive dislike to Gregory, – he was so jealous of the ready love that always gushed out like a spring of fresh water when he came near. He wanted her to love him more, and perhaps that was all well and good; but he

---

taunt: mock, criticise

wanted her to love her child less, and that was an evil wish. One day, he gave way to his temper, and cursed and swore at Gregory, who had got into some mischief, as children will; my mother made some excuse for him; my father said it was hard enough to have to keep another man's child, without having it perpetually held up in its naughtiness by his wife, who ought to be always in the same mind that he was; and so from little they got to more; and the end of it was, that my mother took to her bed **before her time**, and I was born that very day.

My father was glad, and proud, and sorry, all in a breath; glad and proud that a son was born to him; and sorry for his poor wife's state, and to think how his angry words had brought it on. But he was a man who liked better to be angry than sorry, so he soon **found out** that it was all Gregory's fault, and owed him an additional grudge for having hastened my birth. He had another grudge against him before long. My mother began to sink the day after I was born. My father sent to Carlisle for doctors, and would have coined his heart's blood into gold to save her, if that could have been; but it could not. My aunt Fanny used to say sometimes, that she thought Helen did not wish to live, and so just let herself die away without trying to take hold on life; but when I questioned her, she owned that my mother did all the doctors bade her do, with the same sort of uncomplaining patience with which she had acted through life.

One of her last requests was to have Gregory laid in her bed by her side, and then she made him take hold of my little hand. Her husband came in while she was looking at us so, and when he bent tenderly over her to ask her how she felt now, and seemed to gaze on us two little half-brothers, with a grave sort of kindliness, she looked up at his face and smiled, almost her first smile at him; and such a sweet smile! as more besides aunt Fanny have said. In an hour she was dead.

Aunt Fanny came to live with us. It was the best thing that could be done. My father would have been glad to return to his old mode of bachelor life, but what could he do with two little

---

before her time: before the baby was due
found out: convinced himself

children? He needed a woman to take care of him, and who so fitting as his wife's elder sister? So she had the charge of me from my birth; and for a time I was weakly, as was but natural, and she was always beside me, night and day watching over me, and my father nearly as anxious as she. For his land had come down from father to son for more than three hundred years, and he would have cared for me merely as his flesh and blood that was to inherit the land after him. But he needed something to love, for all that, to most people, he was a stern, hard man, and he took to me as, I fancy, he had taken to no human being before – as he might have taken to my mother, if she had had no former life for him to be jealous of. I loved him back again right heartily. I loved all around me, I believe, for everybody was kind to me. After a time, I overcame my original weakliness of constitution, and was just a bonny, strong-looking lad whom every passer-by noticed, when my father took me with him to the nearest town.

At home I was the darling of my aunt, the tenderly-beloved of my father, the pet and plaything of the old **domestic**, the 'young master' of the farm-labourers, before whom I played many a lordly antic, assuming a sort of authority which sat oddly enough, I doubt not, on such a baby as I was.

Gregory was three years older than I. Aunt Fanny was always kind to him in deed and in action, but she did not often think about him, she had fallen so completely into the habit of being engrossed by me, from the fact of my having come into her charge as a delicate baby. My father never got over his grudging dislike to his stepson, who had so innocently wrestled with him for the possession of my mother's heart. **I mistrust me**, too, that my father always considered him as the cause of my mother's death and my early delicacy; and utterly unreasonable as this may seem, I believe my father rather cherished his feeling of alienation to my brother as a duty, than strove to repress it.

Yet not for the world would my father have grudged him anything that money could purchase. That was, as it were, in

domestic: female servant
I mistrust me: I suspect

the bond when he had wedded my mother. Gregory was lumpish and loutish, awkward and ungainly, marring whatever he meddled in, and many a hard word and sharp scolding did he get from the people about the farm, who hardly waited till my father's back was turned before they **rated** the stepson. I am ashamed – my heart is sore to think how I fell into the fashion of the family, and slighted my poor orphan step-brother. I don't think I ever **scouted** him, or was wilfully ill-natured to him; but the habit of being considered in all things, and being treated as something uncommon and superior, made me insolent in my prosperity, and I exacted more than Gregory was always willing to grant, and then, irritated, I sometimes repeated the **disparaging** words I had heard others use with regard to him, without fully understanding their meaning. Whether he did or not I cannot tell. I am afraid he did. He used to turn silent and quiet – sullen and sulky, my father thought it; stupid, aunt Fanny used to call it. But everyone said he was stupid and dull, and this stupidity and dullness grew upon him. He would sit without speaking a word, sometimes, for hours; then my father would bid him rise and do some piece of work, maybe, about the farm. And he would take three or four tellings before he would go.

When we were sent to school, it was all the same. He could never be made to remember his lessons; the schoolmaster grew weary of scolding and flogging, and at last advised my father just to take him away, and set him to some farm-work that might not be above his comprehension. I think he was more gloomy and stupid than ever after this, yet he was not a cross lad; he was patient and good-natured, and would try and do a good turn for any one, even if they had been scolding or cuffing him not a minute before. But very often his attempts at kindness ended in some mischief to the very people he was trying to serve, owing to his awkward, ungainly ways. I suppose I was a clever lad; at any rate, I always got plenty of praise; and was, as we called it, the cock of the school. The schoolmaster

---

rated: scolded
scouted: physically abused
disparaging: insulting

said I could learn anything I chose, but my father, who had no great learning himself, saw little use in much for me, and took me away **betimes**, and kept me with him about the farm. Gregory was made into a kind of shepherd, receiving his training under old Adam, who was nearly past his work.

I think old Adam was almost the first person who had a good opinion of Gregory. He stood to it that my brother had good parts, though he did not rightly know how to bring them out; and, for knowing the bearings of the Fells, he said he had never seen a lad like him. My father would try to bring Adam round to speak of Gregory's faults and shortcomings; but, instead of that, he would praise him twice as much as soon as he found out what was my father's object.

One winter-time, when I was about sixteen, and Gregory nineteen, I was sent by my father on an errand to a place about seven miles distant by the road, but only about four by the Fells. He bade me return by the road, whichever way I took in going, for the evenings closed in early, and were often thick and misty; besides which, old Adam, now **paralytic** and bedridden, foretold a downfall of snow before long. I soon got to my journey's end, and soon had done my business; earlier by an hour, I thought, than my father had expected, so I took the decision of the way by which I would return into my own hands, and set off back again over the Fells, just as the first shades of evening began to fall. It looked dark and gloomy enough; but everything was so still that I thought I should have plenty of time to get home before the snow came down.

Off I set at a pretty quick pace. But night came on quicker. The right path was clear enough in the daytime, although at several points two or three exactly similar diverged from the same place; but when there was a good light, the traveller was guided by the sight of distant objects – a piece of rock, – a fall in the ground – which were quite invisible to me now. I plucked up a brave heart, however, and took what seemed to me the right road. It was wrong, however, and led me whither I knew

---

betimes: early
paralytic: paralysed by a stroke

not, but to some wild boggy moor where the solitude seemed painful, intense, as if never footfall of man had come thither to break the silence. I tried to shout, – with the dimmest possible hope of being heard – rather to reassure myself by the sound of my own voice; but my voice came husky and short, and yet it dismayed me; it seemed so weird and strange in that noiseless expanse of black darkness.

Suddenly the air was filled thick with dusky flakes, my face and hands were wet with snow. It cut me off from the slightest knowledge of where I was, for I lost every idea of the direction from which I had come, so that I could not even retrace my steps; it hemmed me in, thicker, thicker, with a darkness that might be felt. The boggy soil on which I stood quaked under me if I remained long in one place, and yet I dared not move far. All my youthful hardiness seemed to leave me at once. I was on the point of crying, and only very shame seemed to keep it down. To save myself from shedding tears, I shouted – terrible, wild shouts for bare life they were. I turned sick as I paused to listen; no answering sound came but the unfeeling echoes. Only the noiseless, pitiless snow kept falling thicker, thicker – faster, faster!

I was growing numb and sleepy. I tried to move about, but I dared not go far, for fear of the precipices which, I knew, abounded in certain places on the Fells. Now and then, I stood still and shouted again; but my voice was getting choked with tears, as I thought of the desolate, helpless death I was to die, and how little they at home, sitting round the warm, red, bright fire, **wotted** what was become of me, – and how my poor father would grieve for me – it would kill him – it would break his heart, poor old man! Aunt Fanny too – was this to be the end of all her cares for me? I began to review my life in a strange kind of vivid dream, in which the various scenes of my few boyish years passed before me like visions. In a pang of agony, caused by such remembrance of my short life, I gathered up my strength and called out once more, a long, despairing, wailing cry, to which I had no hope of obtaining any answer, save from

---

wotted: knew

the echoes around, dulled as the sound might be by the thickened air.

To my surprise, I heard a cry – almost as long, as wild as mine – so wild that it seemed unearthly, and I almost thought it must be the voice of some of the mocking spirits of the Fells, about whom I had heard so many tales. My heart suddenly began to beat fast and loud. I could not reply for a minute or two. I nearly fancied I had lost the power of utterance. Just at this moment a dog barked. Was it Lassie's bark – my brother's collie? – an ugly enough brute, with a white, ill-looking face, that my father always kicked whenever he saw it, partly for its own **demerits**, partly because it belonged to my brother. On such occasions, Gregory would whistle Lassie away, and go off and sit with her in some outhouse. My father had once or twice been ashamed of himself, when the poor collie had yowled out with the suddenness of the pain, and had relieved himself of his self-reproach by blaming my brother, who, he said, had no notion of training a dog, and was enough to ruin any collie in Christendom with his stupid way of allowing them to lie by the kitchen fire. To all which Gregory would answer nothing, nor even seem to hear, but go on looking absent and moody.

Yes! there again! It was Lassie's bark! Now or never! I lifted up my voice and shouted 'Lassie! Lassie! For God's sake, Lassie!' Another moment, and the great white-faced Lassie was curving and gambolling with delight round my feet and legs, looking, however, up in my face with her intelligent, apprehensive eyes, as if fearing lest I might greet her with a blow, as I had done oftentimes before. But I cried with gladness, as I stooped down and patted her. My mind was sharing in my body's weakness, and I could not reason, but I knew that help was at hand. A grey figure came more and more distinctly out of the thick, close-pressing darkness. It was Gregory wrapped in his **maud**.

'Oh, Gregory!' said I, and I fell upon his neck, unable to speak another word. He never spoke much, and made me no answer for some little time. Then he told me we must move, we

---

demerits: faults
maud: thick woollen cloak

must walk for dear life – we must find our road home, if possible; but we must move or we should be frozen to death.

'Don't you know the way home?' asked I.

'I thought I did when I set out, but I am doubtful now. The snow blinds me, and I am feared that in moving about just now, I have lost the right gait homewards.'

He had his shepherd's staff with him, and by dint of plunging it before us at every step we took – clinging close to each other, we went on safely enough, as far as not falling down any of the steep rocks, but it was slow, dreary work. My brother, I saw, was more guided by Lassie and the way she took than anything else, trusting to her instinct. It was too dark to see far before us; but he called her back continually, and noted from what **quarter** she returned, and shaped our slow steps accordingly. But the tedious motion scarcely kept my blood from freezing. Every bone, every fibre in my body seemed first to ache, and then to swell, and then to turn numb with the intense cold. My brother bore it better than I, from having been more out upon the hills. He did not speak, except to call Lassie. I strove to be brave, and not complain; but now I felt the deadly fatal sleep stealing over me.

'I can go no further,' I said, in a drowsy tone. I remember I suddenly became dogged and resolved. Sleep I would, were it only for five minutes. If death were to be the consequence, sleep I would. Gregory stood still. I suppose he recognised the peculiar phase of suffering to which I had been brought by the cold.

'It is of no use,' said he, as if to himself. 'We are no nearer home than we were when we started, as far as I can tell. Our only chance is Lassie. Here! roll thee in my maud, lad, and lay thee down on this sheltered side of this bit of rock. Creep close under it, lad, and I'll lie by thee, and strive to keep the warmth in us. Stay! hast gotten aught about thee that they'll know at home?'

I felt him unkind thus to keep me from slumber, but on his repeating the question, I pulled out my pocket-handkerchief, of

---

quarter: direction

some showy pattern, which aunt Fanny had hemmed for me – Gregory took it, and tied it round Lassie's neck.

'Hie thee, Lassie, hie thee home!' And the white-faced, ill-favoured brute was off like a shot in the darkness. Now I might lie down – now I might sleep. In my drowsy stupor I felt that I was being tenderly covered up by my brother; but what with I neither knew or cared – I was too dull, too selfish, too numb to think and reason, or I might have known that in that bleak bare place there was naught to wrap me in, save what was taken off another. I was glad enough when he ceased his cares and lay down by me. I took his hand.

'Thou canst not remember, lad, how we lay together thus by our dying mother. She put thy small, wee hand in mine – I reckon she sees us now; and belike we shall soon be with her. Anyhow, God's will be done.'

'Dear Gregory,' I muttered, and crept nearer to him for warmth. He was talking still, and again about our mother, when I fell asleep. In an instant – or so it seemed – there were many voices about me – many faces hovering round me – the sweet luxury of warmth was stealing into every part of me. I was in my own little bed at home. I am thankful to say, my first word was 'Gregory?'

A look passed from one to another – my father's stern old face strove in vain to keep its sternness; his mouth quivered, his eyes filled slowly with unwonted tears.

'I would have given him half my land – I would have blessed him as my son, – oh God! I would have knelt at his feet, and asked him to forgive my hardness of heart.'

I heard no more. A whirl came through my brain, catching me back to death.

I came slowly to my consciousness, weeks afterwards. My father's hair was white when I recovered, and his hands shook as he looked into my face.

We spoke no more of Gregory. We could not speak of him; but he was strangely in our thoughts. Lassie came and went with never a word of blame; nay, my father would try to stroke her, but she shrank away; and he, as if reproved by the poor dumb beast, would sigh, and be silent and abstracted for a time.

Aunt Fanny – always a talker – told me all. How, on that fatal night, my father, irritated by my prolonged absence, and probably more anxious than he cared to show, had been fierce and imperious, even **beyond his wont**, to Gregory: had **upbraided** him with his father's poverty, his own stupidity which made his services good for nothing – for so, in spite of the old shepherd, my father always chose to consider them. At last, Gregory had risen up, and whistled Lassie out with him – poor Lassie, crouching underneath his chair for fear of a kick or a blow. Some time before, there had been some talk between my father and my aunt respecting my return; and when aunt Fanny told me all this, she said she fancied that Gregory might have noticed the coming storm, and gone out silently to meet me.

Three hours afterwards, when all were running about in wild alarm, not knowing whither to go in search of me – not even missing Gregory, or heeding his absence, poor fellow – poor, poor fellow! – Lassie came home, with my handkerchief tied round her neck. They knew and understood, and the whole strength of the farm was turned out to follow her, with wraps, and blankets, and brandy, and everything that could be thought of. I lay in chilly sleep, but still alive, beneath the rock that Lassie guided them to. I was covered over with my brother's plaid, and his thick shepherd's coat was carefully wrapped round my feet. He was in his shirt-sleeves – his arm thrown over me – a quiet smile (he had hardly ever smiled in life) upon his still, cold face.

My father's last words were, 'God forgive me my hardness of heart towards the fatherless child!'

And what marked the depth of his feeling of repentance, perhaps more than all, considering the passionate love he bore my mother, was this: we found a paper of directions after his death, in which he desired that he might lie at the foot of the grave, in which, by his desire, poor Gregory had been laid with our mother.

---

beyond his wont: more than usual
upbraided: reproached

Non-fiction passages linked to *The Half-Brother* (1858)

Infant mortality in the mid-nineteenth century

a The death of Helen's daughter in early childhood was not unusual:

Epidemic diseases were frequent and fatal. As an instance, I remember being in bed with my brothers James and Robert, when I was hurriedly taken out of bed and carried away to a cottage several miles distant by a friend of my mother's. I did not see my home for a long time, six months, as I was told afterwards. When I was brought home again, my playmates were gone. Black fever had almost emptied the house. My four brothers and sisters had all died and I was the only one that remained of five.

William Webb, 1880

b Like Helen's daughter, Elizabeth Gaskell's only son died of scarlet fever. He was ten months old.

c Victorian children chanted this rhyme as part of a street game:

> Grandmother, Grandmother
> Tell me the Truth,
> How many years am I
> Going to Live?
> One, Two, Three, Four …

Traditional

d Of those who died in London between 1810 and 1829, 31.8 per cent were children below the age of five.

HMSO

The need for Victorian women to marry

a Before her re-marriage, Helen's employment at home as an 'out-worker' would have been arduous and badly-paid:

Recently I visited a maker of blouses who was concocting with much taste and skill blouses of white muslin, trimmed with embroidery. These would probably sell in the shops for but a few shillings, yet the labour involved was not insignificant, for there was much tucking and trimming. The blouse-maker was a young woman, and, having a small child to look after, could not easily go out as a dress maker. Yet her occupation was fully as laborious. During the months before Christmas, she was obliged by her employer to make none but pattern blouses, that is to say, bodices of her own designing, no two being alike. She told me that she found this business of designing was most trying, and that she often lost her rest at night trying to think of some new style. The payment she received, 2s. 6d. a dozen, did not pay her for the increase of time and thought involved. She had to make from three to six blouses a day.

Charles Kingsley, 1850

b In Helen's position, re-marriage to a man who could provide for herself and Gregory was essential:

Social and economic pressures, as well as the law, made it very difficult for Victorian women to choose a single life. The plight of the woman who did not marry, who in the parlance of the age was 'left on the shelf', could be economically as well as socially disastrous. The average wage that working-class women could command was below subsistence level. Legal rules, social practices and economic structures all worked together to induce a woman to marry, and then ensured that once married she would be utterly dependent upon her husband.

Mary Lyndon Shanley, 1989

The Parvenue
Mary Shelley

Why do I write my melancholy story? Is it as a lesson, to prevent any other from wishing to rise to rank superior to that in which they are born? No, miserable as I am, others might have been happy, I doubt not, in my position: the **chalice** has been poisoned for me alone! Am I evil-minded – am I wicked? What have been my errors, that I am now an outcast and wretched? I will tell you my story – let others judge me; my mind is bewildered, I cannot judge myself.

My father was land steward to a wealthy nobleman. He married young, and had several children. He then lost his wife, and remained fifteen years a widower, when he married again a young girl, the daughter of a clergyman who died leaving numerous offspring in extreme poverty. My maternal grandfather had been a man of sensibility and genius; my mother inherited many of his endowments. She was an angel on earth; all her works were charity, all her thoughts were love.

Within a year after her marriage, she gave birth to twins – I and my sister; soon after she fell into ill-health, and from that time was always weakly. She could endure no fatigue, and seldom moved from her chair. I see her now; – her white, delicate hands employed in needlework, her soft, love-lighted eyes fixed on me. I was still a child when my father fell into trouble, and we removed from the part of the country where we had hitherto lived, and went to a distant village, where we rented a cottage, with a little land adjoining. We were poor, and all the family assisted each other. My elder half-sisters were strong, industrious, rustic young women, and submitted to a life of labour with great cheerfulness. My father held the plough, my half-brothers worked in the barns; all was toil, yet all seemed enjoyment.

parvenue: a low-class person who rises up in society
chalice: cup

How happy my childhood was! Hand in hand with my dear twin-sister, I plucked the spring flowers in the hedges, turned the hay in the summer meadows, shook the apples from the trees in the autumn, and at all seasons, gambolled in delicious liberty beneath the free air of heaven; or at my mother's feet, caressed by her, I was taught the sweetest lessons of charity and love. My elder sisters were kind; we were all linked by strong affection. The delicate, fragile existence of my mother gave an interest to our monotony, while her virtues and her refinement threw a grace over our homely household.

I and my sister did not seem twins, we were so unlike. She was robust, chubby, full of life and spirits; I, tall, slim, fair, and even pale. I loved to play with her, but soon grew tired, and then I crept to my mother's side, and she sang me to sleep, and nursed me in her bosom, and looked on me with her own angelic smile. She took pains to instruct me, not in accomplishments, but in all real knowledge. She unfolded to me the wonders of the visible creation, and to each tale of bird and beast, of fiery mountain or vast river, was appended some moral, derived from her warm heart and ardent imagination. Above all, she impressed upon me the **precepts of the gospel**, charity to every fellow-creature, the brotherhood of mankind, the rights that every sentient creature possesses to our service. I was her **almoner**; for, poor as she was, she was the **benefactress** of those who were poorer. Being delicate, I helped her in her task of needlework, while my sister aided the rest in their household or rustic labours.

When I was seventeen, a miserable accident happened. A hayrick caught fire; it communicated to our outhouses, and at last to the cottage. We were roused from our beds at midnight, and escaped barely with our lives. My father bore out my mother in his arms, and then tried to save a portion of his property. The roof of the cottage fell on him. He was dug out after an hour, scorched, maimed, crippled for life.

---

precepts of the gospel: bible teachings
almoner: a person who takes help to the poor
benefactress: a woman who gives charity to the poor

We were all saved, but by a miracle only was I preserved. I and my sister were awoke by cries of fire. The cottage was already enveloped in flames. Susan, with her accustomed **intrepidity**, rushed through the flames, and escaped; I thought only of my mother, and hurried to her room. The fire raged around me; it encircled – hemmed me in. I believed that I must die, when suddenly I felt myself seized upon and borne away. I looked on my preserver – it was Lord Reginald Desborough.

For many Sundays past, when at church, I knew that Lord Reginald's eyes were fixed on me. He had met me and Susan in our walks; he had called at our cottage. There was fascination in his eye, in his soft voice and earnest gaze, and my heart throbbed with gladness, as I thought that he surely loved me. To have been saved by him was to make the **boon** of life doubly precious.

There is to me much obscurity in this part of my story. Lord Reginald loved me, it is true; why he loved me, so far as to forget pride of rank and ambition for my sake, he who afterwards showed no tendency to disregard the prejudices and habits of rank and wealth, I cannot tell; it seems strange. He had loved me before, but from the hour that he saved my life, love grew into an overpowering passion. He offered us a lodge on his estate to take refuge in; and while there, he sent us presents of **game**, and still more kindly, fruits and flowers to my mother, and came himself, especially when all were out except my mother and myself, and sat by us and conversed. Soon I learnt to expect the soft asking look of his eyes, and almost dared answer it. My mother once perceived these glances, and took an opportunity to appeal to Lord Reginald's good feelings, not to make me miserable for life, by implanting an attachment that could only be productive of unhappiness. His answer was to ask me in marriage.

I need not say that my mother gratefully consented; that my father, confined to his bed since the fire, thanked God with rapture; that my sisters were transported by delight: I was the

intrepidity: fearlessness
boon: blessing
game: animals and birds hunted for food

least surprised then, though the most happy. Now, I wonder much, what could he see in me? So many girls of rank and fortune were prettier. I was an untaught, low-born, **portionless** girl. It was very strange.

Then I only thought of the happiness of marrying him, of being loved, of passing my life with him. My wedding day was fixed. Lord Reginald had neither father nor mother to interfere with his arrangements. He told no relation; he became one of our family during the interval. He saw no deficiencies in our mode of life – in my dress; he was satisfied with all; he was tender, assiduous, and kind, even to my elder sisters; he seemed to adore my mother, and became a brother to my sister Susan. She was in love, and asked him to intercede to gain her parents' consent for her choice. He did so; and though before, Lawrence Cooper, the carpenter of the place, had been disdained, supported by him, he was accepted. Lawrence Cooper was young, well-looking, well disposed, and fondly attached to Susan.

My wedding day came. My mother kissed me fondly, my father blessed me with pride and joy, my sisters stood round, radiant with delight. There was but one drawback to the universal happiness – that immediately on my marriage I was to go abroad.

From the church door I stepped into the carriage. Having once and again been folded in my dear mother's embrace, the wheels were in motion, and we were away. I looked out from the window; there was the dear group: my old father, white-headed and aged, in his large chair; my mother, smiling through her tears, with folded hands and upraised looks of gratitude, anticipating long years of happiness for her child; Susan and Lawrence standing side by side, unenvious of my greatness, happy in themselves; my sisters **conning** over with pride and joy the presents made to them, and the prosperity that flowed in from my husband's generosity. All looked happy, and it seemed as if I were the cause of all this happiness. We had been indeed saved from dreadful evils; ruin had ensued

---

portionless: without a dowry, penniless
conning: looking

from the fire, and we had been sunk in adversity through that very event from which our good fortune took its rise. I felt proud and glad. I loved them all. I thought, I make them happy – they are prosperous through me! And my heart warmed with gratitude towards my husband at the idea.

We spent two years abroad. It was rather lonely for me, who had always been surrounded, as it were, by a populous world of my own, to find myself cast upon foreigners and strangers; the habits of the different sexes in the higher ranks so separate them from each other, that, after a few months, I spent much of my time in solitude. I did not **repine**; I had been brought up to look upon the hard **visage** of life, if not unflinchingly, at least with resignation. I did not expect perfect happiness. Marriages in humble life are attended with so much care. I had none of this; my husband loved me; and though I often longed to see the dear familiar faces that thronged my childhood's home, and, above all, pined for my mother's caresses and her wise maternal lessons, yet for a time I was content to think of them, and hope for a reunion.

Still many things pained me. I had, poor myself, been brought up among the poor, and nothing, since I can remember forming an idea, so much astonished and jarred with my feelings as the thought of how the rich could spend so much on themselves, while any of their fellow-creatures were in destitution. I had none of the **patrician** charity (though such is praise-worthy), which consists in distributing thin soup and coarse flannel petticoats – a sort of instinct or sentiment of justice, the offspring of my lowly paternal hearth, and my mother's enlightened **piety**, was deeply implanted in my mind, that all had as good a right to the comforts of life as myself, or even as my husband. My charities, they were called – they seemed to me the payment of my debts to my fellow-creatures – were abundant. Lord Reginald **peremptorily checked** them;

---

repine: complain
visage: face
patrician: upper-class
piety: Christian goodness
peremptorily checked: abruptly stopped

but as I had a large allowance for my own expenses, I denied myself a thousand luxuries, for the sake of feeding the hungry. Nor was it only that charity impelled me, but that I could not acquire a taste for spending money on myself – I disliked the **apparatus** of wealth. My husband called my ideas sordid, and reproved me severely, when, instead of outshining all competitors at a fete, I appeared dowdily dressed, and declared warmly that I could not, I would not, spend twenty guineas for a gown, while I could dress many sad faces in smiles, and bring much joy to many drooping hearts, by the same sum.

Was I right? I firmly believe that there is not one among the rich who will not affirm that I did wrong; that to please my husband, and do honour to his rank, was my first duty. Yet, shall I confess it? even now, rendered miserable by this fault – I cannot give it that name – I can call it a misfortune – I have wasted at the slow fire of knowing that I lost my husband's affections because I performed what I believed to be a duty.

But I am not come to that yet. It was not till my return to England that the full disaster crushed me. We had often been applied to for money by my family, and Lord Reginald had acceded to nearly all their requests. When we reached London, after two years' absence, my first wish was to see my dear mother. She was at Margate for her health. It was agreed that I should go there alone, and pay a short visit. Before I went, Lord Reginald told me what I did not know before, that my family had often made exorbitant demands on him, with which he was resolved not to comply. He told me that he had no wish to raise my relatives from their station in society; and that, indeed, there were only two among them whom he conceived had any claims upon me – my mother and my twin-sister: that the former was incapable of any improper request, and the latter, by marrying Cooper, had fixed her own position, and could in no way be raised from the rank of her chosen husband. I agreed to much that he said. I replied that he well knew that my own taste led me to consider **mediocrity** the best and happiest

---

apparatus: outward show
mediocrity: ordinariness

situation; that I had no wish, and would never consent, to supply any extravagant demands on the part of persons, however dear to me, whose circumstances he had rendered easy.

Satisfied with my reply, we parted most affectionately, and I went on my way to Margate with a light and glad heart; and the cordial reception I received from my whole family collected together to receive me, was calculated to add to my satisfaction. The only drawback to my content was my mother's state; she was wasted to a shadow. They all talked and laughed around her, but it was evident to me that she had not long to live.

There was no room for me in the small furnished house in which they were all crowded, so I remained at the hotel. Early in the morning, before I was up, my father visited me. He begged me to intercede with my husband; that on the strength of his support he had embarked on a speculation which required a large capital; that many families would be ruined, and himself dishonoured, if a few hundreds were not advanced. I promised to do what I could, resolving to ask my mother's advice, and make her my guide. My father kissed me with an effusion of gratitude, and left me.

I cannot enter into the whole of these sad details; all my half-brothers and sisters had married, and trusted to their success in life to Lord Reginald's assistance. Each evidently thought they asked little in not demanding an equal share of my luxuries and fortune; but they were all in difficulty – all needed large assistance – all depended on me.

Lastly, my own sister Susan appealed to me – but hers was the most moderate request of all – she only wished for twenty pounds. I gave it her at once from my own purse.

As soon as I saw my mother I explained to her my difficulties. She told me that she expected this, and that it broke her heart: I must summon courage and resist these demands. That my father's imprudence had ruined him, and that he must encounter the evil he had brought upon himself; that my numerous relatives were absolutely mad with the notion of what I ought to do for them. I listened with grief – I saw the torments in store for me – I felt my own weakness, and knew that I could not meet the **rapacity** of those about me with any courage or firmness. That same night my mother fell into convulsions; her life was saved with difficulty. From Susan I learned the cause of her attack. She had had a violent **altercation** with my father: she insisted that I should not be appealed to; while he reproached her for rendering me undutiful, and bringing ruin and disgrace on his grey hairs. When I saw my pale mother trembling, fainting, dying – when I was again and again assured that she must be my father's victim unless I yielded, what wonder that, in the agony of my distress, I wrote to my husband to implore his assistance.

Oh, what thick clouds now obscured my destiny! how do I remember, with a sort of thrilling horror, the boundless sea, white cliffs, and wide sands of Margate! The summer day that had welcomed my arrival changed to bleak wintry weather during this interval – while I waited with anguish for my husband's answer. Well do I remember the evening on which it came: the waves of the sea showed their white crests, no vessel ventured to meet the gale with any canvas except a topsail, the sky was bared clear by the wind, the sun was going down fiery red. I looked upon the troubled waters – I longed to be borne away upon them, away from care and misery. At this moment a servant followed me to the sands with my husband's answer – it contained a refusal. I dared not communicate it. The menaces of bankruptcy; the knowledge that he had instilled false hopes into so many; the fears of disgrace, rendered my father, always rough, absolutely ferocious. Life flickered in my dear mother's frame, it seemed on the point of expiring when she heard my father's step; if he came in with a smooth brow, her pale lips wreathed into her own sweet smile, and a delicate pink tinged her fallen cheeks; if he scowled, and his voice was high, every limb shivered, she turned her face to her pillow, while convulsive tears shook her frame, and threatened instant **dissolution**. My father sought me alone one day, as I was walking in melancholy guise upon the sands; he swore that he

---

rapacity: savage greed
altercation: argument
dissolution: death

would not survive his disgrace. 'And do you think, Fanny,' he added, 'that your mother will survive the knowledge of my miserable end?' I saw the resolution of despair in his face as he spoke. – I asked the sum needed, the time when it must be given. – A thousand pounds in two days was all that was asked. I set off to London to implore my husband to give this sum.

No! no! I cannot step by step record my wretchedness – the money was given – I extorted it from Lord Reginald, though I saw his heart closed on me as he wrote the cheque. Worse had happened since I had left him. Susan had used the twenty pounds I gave her to reach town, to throw herself at my husband's feet, and implore his compassion. Rendered absolutely insane by the idea of having a lord for a brother-in-law, Cooper had launched into a system of extravagance, incredible as it was wicked. He was many thousands of pounds in debt, and when at last Lord Reginald wrote to refuse all further supply, the miserable man committed forgery. Two hundred pounds prevented exposure, and preserved him from an **ignominious** end. Five hundred more were advanced to send him and his wife to America, to settle there, out of the way of temptation. I parted from my dear sister – I loved her fondly; she had no part in her husband's guilt, yet she was still attached to him, and her child bound them together; they went into solitary, miserable exile. 'Ah! had we remained in virtuous poverty,' cried my broken-hearted sister, 'I had not been forced to leave my dying mother.'

The thousand pounds given to my father was but a drop of water in the ocean. Again I was appealed to; again I felt the slender thread of my mother's life depended on my getting a supply. Again, trembling and miserable, I implored the charity of my husband.

'I am content,' he said, 'to do what you ask, to do more than you ask; but remember the price you pay – either give up your parents and your family, whose rapacity and crimes deserve no mercy, or we part for ever. You shall have a proper allowance; you can maintain all your family on it if you please; but their

---

ignominious: shameful

names must never be mentioned to me again. Choose between us – you never see them more, or we part for ever.'

Did I do right – I cannot tell – misery is the result – misery frightful, endless, unredeemed. My mother was dearer to me than all the world. I did not reply – I rushed to my room, and that night, in a delirium of grief and horror, I set out for Margate – such was my reply to my husband.

Three years have passed since then; and during all this time I was grateful to Heaven for being permitted to do my duty by my mother; and though I wept over the **alienation** of my husband, I did not repent. But she, my angelic support, is no more. My father survived my mother but two months; remorse for all he had done, and made me suffer, cut short his life. His family by his first wife are gathered round me; they **importune**, they rob, they destroy me. Last week I wrote to Lord Reginald. I communicated the death of my parents; I represented that my position was altered, and that if he still cared for his unhappy wife all might be well. Yesterday his answer came. – It was too late, he said: – I had myself torn asunder the ties that united us – they never could be knit together again.

By the same post came a letter from Susan. She is happy. Cooper, awakened to a manly sense of the duties of life, is thoroughly transformed. He is industrious and prosperous. Susan asks me to join her. I am resolved to go. Oh! my home, and recollections of my youth, where are ye now? **envenomed** by serpents' stings, I long to close my eyes on every scene I have ever viewed. Let me seek a strange land, a land where a grave will soon be opened for me. I desire to die. I am told that Lord Reginald loves another, a high-born girl; that he openly curses our union as the obstacle to his happiness. The memory of this will poison the oblivion I go to seek. He will soon be free. Soon will the hand he once so fondly took in his and made his own, which, now flung away, trembles with misery as it traces these lines, moulder in its last decay.

---

alienation: isolation
importune: beg
envenomed: poisoned

Non-fiction passages linked to *The Parvenue* (1848)

The role of a wife in Victorian times

a Her duty:

> A woman's highest duty is so
> often to suffer and be still.

Mrs Sarah Stickney Evans, 1845

b A willing slave:

> All men desire to have, in the woman most nearly
> connected with them, not a forced slave but a
> willing one. All women are brought up from the very
> earliest years in the belief that their ideal of character
> is the very opposite of that of men: not self-will and
> government but submission and yielding to the control
> of others.

John Stuart Mill, 1861

c Her husband's 'helpmeet':

THE VICTORIAN WIFE was considered the 'helpmeet' of her husband. As the man achieved his position in the cruel, harsh, competitive outside world, he sought refuge in his home, which became his sanctuary. As her husband's 'helpmeet', the Victorian wife was to provide the proper environment of respectability. She became the guardian of morality, the citadel of respectability. 'Helpmeet' to her husband required that she be righteous, gentle, sympathetic, and most of all submissive. This image ensured the inferior relationship of the wife to the husband.

Patricia Branca, 1975

d The home-maker:

This is the true nature of home – it is the place of peace; the shelter, not only from all injury, but from all terror, doubt, and division … And wherever the true wife comes, this home is always round her. The stars only may be over her head, the glow-worm in the night-cold grass may be the only fire at her feet, but home is wherever she is; and for a noble woman it stretches far round her, shedding its quiet light far for those who else were homeless.

John Ruskin, 1864

Separation and divorce in the mid-nineteenth century

a The legal rights of both married and separated women were almost non-existent. The law favoured husbands:

Until recent times, it was extremely difficult and rare for a woman to divorce her husband and, however bad his behaviour, her own reputation would be ruined if she did so. The law was unjust. A man could divorce his wife for adultery but she could not divorce him, however unfaithful he was, unless he committed an additional matrimonial offence such as incest or cruelty which were extremely difficult to prove. Even then, there was little chance of forcing an unwilling husband to pay maintenance.

The legal view was that women were not merely dependent on their husbands, but had no separate legal identity of their own. Sir William Blackstone had written in his *Commentaries on the Laws of England*, 'By marriage, the very being or legal existence of woman is suspended, or at least it is incorporated into that of the husband, under whose wing and cover she performs everything. She is therefore called in law a feme-covert.' A wife was unable to enter into legal contracts and had no rights in her own property. All she had, earned or inherited, was deemed to belong to her husband.

Angela Holdsworth, 1988

b A separated wife on living apart from her husband:

ALONE. Married to a man's name, but never to know the protection of this nominal husband, nor the joys of family, nor the every-day companionship of a real home. Never to feel or show preference for any friend not of her own sex. To be slandered, tormented, insulted; to find the world and the world's law utterly indifferent to her wrongs or her husband's sin. And through all this to live a chaste, unspotted, patient, cheerful life; without anger, without bitterness, and with meek respect for those laws which pronounce that it 'is not good for man to be alone' but extremely good for woman.

Caroline Norton, 1853

To Please His Wife

Thomas Hardy

ONE

The interior of St James's Church, in Havenpool Town, was
slowly darkening under the close clouds of a winter afternoon.
It was Sunday; service had just ended, the face of the parson in
the pulpit was buried in his hands, and the congregation, with
a cheerful sigh of release, were rising from their knees to depart.

For the moment the stillness was so complete that the
surging of the sea could be heard outside the harbour-bar.
Then it was broken by the footsteps of the clerk going towards
the west door to open it in the usual manner for the exit of the
assembly. Before, however, he had reached the doorway, the
latch was lifted from without, and the dark figure of a man in a
sailor's garb appeared against the light.

The clerk stepped aside, the sailor closed the door gently
behind him, and advanced up the nave till he stood at the
chancel-step. The parson looked up from the private little
prayer which, after so many for the parish, he quite fairly took
for himself, rose to his feet, and stared at the intruder.

'I beg your pardon, sir,' said the sailor, addressing the
minister in a voice distinctly audible to all the congregation. 'I
have come here to offer thanks for my narrow escape from
shipwreck. I am given to understand that it is a proper thing to
do, if you have no objection?'

The parson, after a moment's pause, said hesitatingly, 'I have
no objection; certainly. It is usual to mention any such wish
before service, so that the proper words may be used in the
General Thanksgiving. But, if you wish, we can read from the
form for use after a storm at sea.'

'Ay, sure; I ain't particular,' said the sailor.

The clerk thereupon directed the sailor to the page in the
prayer-book where the collect of thanksgiving would be found,

and the rector began reading it, the sailor kneeling where he stood, and repeating it after him word for word in a distinct voice. The people, who had remained **agape** and motionless at the proceeding, mechanically knelt down likewise, but they continued to regard the isolated form of the sailor who, in the precise middle of the chancel-step, remained fixed on his knees, facing the east, his hat beside him, his hands joined, and he quite unconscious of his appearance in their regard.

When his thanksgiving had come to an end he rose; the people rose also; and all went out of church together. As soon as the sailor emerged, so that the remaining daylight fell upon his face, old inhabitants began to recognize him as none other than Shadrach Jolliffe, a young man who had not been seen at Havenpool for several years. A son of the town, his parents had died when he was quite young, on which account he had early gone to sea, in the Newfoundland trade.

He talked with this and that townsman as he walked, informing them that, since leaving his native place years before, he had become captain and owner of a small coasting-ketch, which had **providentially** been saved from the gale as well as himself. Presently he drew near to two girls who were going out of the churchyard in front of him; they had been sitting in the nave at his entry, and had watched his doings with deep interest, afterwards discussing him as they moved out of church together. One was a slight and gentle creature, the other a tall, large-framed, deliberative girl. Captain Jolliffe regarded the loose curls of their hair, their backs and shoulders, down to their heels, for some time.

'Who may them two maids be?' he whispered to his neighbour.

'The little one is Emily Hanning; the tall one Joanna Phippard.'

'Ah! I recollect 'em now, to be sure.'

He advanced to their elbow, and genially stole a gaze at them.

---

agape: astonished
providentially: by God's goodness

'Emily, you don't know me?' said the sailor, turning his beaming brown eyes on her.

'I think I do, Mr Jolliffe,' said Emily shyly.

The other girl looked straight at him with her dark eyes.

'The face of Miss Joanna I don't call to mind so well,' he continued. 'But I know her beginnings and kindred.'

They walked and talked together, Jolliffe narrating particulars of his late narrow escape, till they reached the corner of Sloop Lane, in which Emily Hanning dwelt, when, with a nod and smile, she left them. Soon the sailor parted also from Joanna, and, having no especial errand or appointment, turned back towards Emily's house. She lived with her father, who called himself an accountant, the daughter, however, keeping a little stationery-shop as a supplemental provision for the gaps of his somewhat uncertain business. On entering Jolliffe found father and daughter about to begin tea.

'O, I didn't know it was teatime,' he said. 'Ay, I'll have a cup with much pleasure.'

He remained to tea and long afterwards, telling more tales of his seafaring life. Several neighbours called to listen, and were asked to come in. Somehow Emily Hanning lost her heart to the sailor that Sunday night, and in the course of a week or two there was a tender understanding between them.

One moonlight evening in the next month Shadrach was ascending out of the town by the long straight road eastward, to an elevated suburb where the more fashionable houses stood – if anything near this ancient port could be called fashionable – when he saw a figure before him whom, from her manner of glancing back, he took to be Emily. But, on coming up, he found she was Joanna Phippard. He gave a gallant greeting, and walked beside her.

'Go along,' she said, 'or Emily will be jealous!'

He seemed not to like the suggestion, and remained.

What was said and what was done on that walk never could be clearly recollected by Shadrach; but in some way or other Joanna contrived to wean him away from her gentler and younger rival. From that week onwards, Jolliffe was seen more and more in the wake of Joanna Phippard and less in the

company of Emily; and it was soon rumoured about the quay
that old Jolliffe's son, who had come home from sea, was going
to be married to the former young woman, to the great
disappointment of the latter.

Just after this report had gone about, Joanna dressed herself
for a walk one morning, and started for Emily's house in the
little cross-street. **Intelligence** of the deep sorrow of her friend
on account of the loss of Shadrach had reached her ears also,
and her conscience reproached her for winning him away.

Joanna was not altogether satisfied with the sailor. She liked
his attentions, and she **coveted** the dignity of matrimony; but she
had never been deeply in love with Jolliffe. For one thing, she
was ambitious, and socially his position was hardly so good as
her own, and there was always the chance of an attractive woman
mating considerably above her. It had long been in her mind that
she would not strongly object to give him back again to Emily if
her friend felt so very badly about him. To this end she had
written a letter of **renunciation** to Shadrach, which letter she
carried in her hand, intending to send it if personal observation
of Emily convinced her that her friend was suffering.

Joanna entered Sloop Lane and stepped down into the
stationery-shop, which was below the pavement level. Emily's
father was never at home at this hour of the day, and it seemed
as though Emily were not at home either, for the visitor could
make nobody hear. Customers came so seldom hither that a
five minutes' absence of the proprietor counted for little.
Joanna waited in the little shop, where Emily had tastefully set
out – as women can – articles in themselves of slight value, so
as to obscure the meagreness of the stock-in-trade; till she saw
a figure pausing without the window apparently absorbed in
the contemplation of the sixpenny books, packets of paper, and
prints hung on a string. It was Captain Shadrach Jolliffe, peering
in to ascertain if Emily were there alone. Moved by an impulse
of reluctance to meet him in a spot which breathed of Emily,
Joanna slipped through the door that communicated with the

---

intelligence: knowledge
coveted: desired
renunciation: refusal

parlour at the back. She had frequently done so before, for in her friendship with Emily she had the freedom of the house without ceremony.

Jolliffe entered the shop. Through the thin blind which screened the glass partition she could see that he was disappointed at not finding Emily there. He was about to go out again, when Emily's form darkened the doorway, hastening home from some errand. At sight of Jolliffe she started back as if she would have gone out again.

'Don't run away, Emily; don't!' said he. 'What can make 'ee afraid?'

'I'm not afraid, Captain Jolliffe. Only – only I saw you all of a sudden, and – it made me jump!' Her voice showed that her heart had jumped even more than the rest of her.

'I just called as I was passing,' he said.

'For some paper?' She hastened behind the counter.

'No, no, Emily; why do you get behind there? Why not stay by me? You seem to hate me.'

'I don't hate you. How can I?'

'Then come out, so that we can talk like Christians.'

Emily obeyed with a fitful laugh, till she stood again beside him in the open part of the shop.

'There's a dear,' he said.

'You mustn't say that, Captain Jolliffe; because the words belong to somebody else.'

'Ah! I know what you mean. But, Emily, upon my life I didn't know till this morning that you cared one bit about me, or I should not have done as I have done. I have the best of feelings for Joanna, but I know that from the beginning she hasn't cared for me more than in a friendly way; and I see now the one I ought to have asked to be my wife. You know, Emily, when a man comes home from sea after a long voyage he's as blind as a bat – he can't see who's who in women. They are all alike to him, beautiful creatures, and he takes the first that comes easy, without thinking if she loves him, or if he might not soon love another better than her. From the first I inclined to you most, but you were so backward and shy that I thought you didn't want me to bother 'ee, and so I went to Joanna.'

'Don't say any more, Mr Jolliffe, don't!' said she, choking. 'You are going to marry Joanna next month, and it is wrong to – to – '

'O, Emily, my darling!' he cried, and clasped her little figure in his arms before she was aware.

Joanna, behind the curtain, turned pale, tried to withdraw her eyes, but could not.

'It is only you I love as a man ought to love the woman he is going to marry; and I know this from what Joanna has said, that she will willingly let me off! She wants to marry **higher** I know, and only said "Yes" to me out of kindness. A fine, tall girl like her isn't the sort for a plain sailor's wife: you be the best suited for that.'

He kissed her and kissed her again, her flexible form quivering in the agitation of his embrace.

'I wonder – are you sure – Joanna is going to break off with you? O, are you sure? Because – '

'I know she would not wish to make us miserable. She will release me.'

'O I hope – I hope she will! Don't stay any longer, Captain Jolliffe.'

He lingered, however, till a customer came for a penny stick of sealing-wax, and then he withdrew.

Green envy had overspread Joanna at the scene. She looked about for a way of escape. To get out without Emily's knowledge of her visit was indispensable. She crept from the parlour into the passage, and thence to the back door of the house, where she let herself noiselessly into the street.

The sight of that caress had reversed all her resolutions. She could not let Shadrach go. Reaching home she burnt the letter, and told her mother that if Captain Jolliffe called she was too unwell to see him.

Shadrach, however, did not call: He sent her a note expressing in simple language the state of his feelings; and asked to be allowed to take advantage of the hints she had given him that her affection, too, was little more than friendly, by cancelling the engagement.

---

higher: better

Looking out upon the harbour and the island beyond he waited and waited in his lodgings for an answer that did not come. The suspense grew to be so intolerable that after dark he went up the High Street. He could not resist calling at Joanna's to learn his fate.

Her mother said her daughter was too unwell to see him, and to his questioning admitted that it was in consequence of a letter received from himself, which had distressed her deeply.

'You know what it was about, perhaps, Mrs Phippard?' he said.

Mrs Phippard owned that she did, adding that it put them in a very painful position. Thereupon Shadrach, fearing that he had been guilty of an **enormity**, explained that if his letter had pained Joanna it must be owing to a misunderstanding, since he had thought it would be a relief to her. If otherwise, he would hold himself bound by his word, and she was to think of the letter as never having been written.

Next morning he received an oral message from the young woman, asking him to fetch her home from a meeting that evening. This he did, and while walking from the Town Hall to her door, with her hand in his arm, she said:

'It is all the same as before between us, isn't it, Shadrach? Your letter was sent in mistake?'

'It is all the same as before,' he answered, 'if you say it must be.'

'I wish it to be,' she murmured, with **hard lineaments**, as she thought of Emily.

Shadrach was a religious and scrupulous man, who respected his word as his life. Shortly afterwards the wedding took place, Jolliffe having conveyed to Emily as gently as possible the error he had fallen into when estimating Joanna's mood as one of indifference.

---

enormity: serious fault
hard lineaments: stern facial expression

TWO

A month after the marriage Joanna's mother died, and the couple were obliged to turn their attention to very practical matters. Now that she was left without a parent, Joanna could not bear the notion of her husband going to sea again, but the question was, What could he do at home? They finally decided to take on a small grocer's shop in High Street, the goodwill and stock of which were waiting to be disposed of at that time. Shadrach knew nothing of shopkeeping, and Joanna very little, but they hoped to learn.

To the management of this grocery business they now devoted all their energies, and continued to conduct it for many succeeding years, without great success. Two sons were born to them, whom their mother loved to idolatry, although she had never passionately loved her husband; and she lavished upon them all her forethought and care. But the shop did not thrive, and the large dreams she had entertained of her sons' education and career became **attenuated** in the face of realities. Their schooling was of the plainest, but, being by the sea, they grew alert in all such nautical arts and enterprises as were attractive to their age.

The great interest of the Jolliffes' married life, outside their own immediate household, had lain in the marriage of Emily. By one of those odd chances which lead those that lurk in unexpected corners to be discovered, while the obvious are passed by, the gentle girl had been seen and loved by a thriving merchant of the town, a widower, some years older than herself, though still in the prime of life. At first Emily had declared that she never, never could marry anyone; but Mr Lester had quietly persevered, and had at last won her reluctant **assent**. Two children also were the fruits of the union, and, as they grew and prospered, Emily declared that she had never supposed that she could live to be so happy.

The worthy merchant's home, one of those large, substantial brick mansions frequently jammed up in old-fashioned towns,

attenuated: reduced
assent: agreement

faced directly on the High Street, nearly opposite to the grocery shop of the Jolliffes, and it now became the pain of Joanna to behold the woman whose place she had usurped out of pure covetousness, looking down from her position of comparative wealth upon the humble shop-window with its dusty sugar-loaves, heaps of raisins, and canisters of tea, over which it was her own lot to preside. The business having so dwindled, Joanna was obliged to serve in the shop herself, and it galled and mortified her that Emily Lester, sitting in her large drawing-room over the way, could witness her own dancings up and down behind the counter at the beck and call of wretched twopenny customers, whose **patronage** she was driven to welcome gladly: persons to whom she was compelled to be civil in the street, while Emily was bounding along with her children and governess, and conversing with the **genteelest** people of the town and neighbourhood. This was what she had gained by not letting Shadrach Jolliffe, whom she had so faintly loved, carry his affection elsewhere.

Shadrach was a good and honest man, and he had been faithful to her in heart and in deed. Time had clipped the wings of his love for Emily in his devotion to the mother of his boys: he had quite lived down that impulsive earlier fancy, and Emily had become in his regard nothing more than a friend. It was the same with Emily's feelings for him. Possibly, had she found the least cause for jealousy, Joanna would almost have been better satisfied. It was in the absolute acquiescence of Emily and Shadrach in the results she herself had contrived that her discontent found nourishment.

Shadrach was not endowed with the narrow shrewdness necessary for developing a retail business in the face of many competitors. Did a customer inquire if the grocer could really recommend the wondrous substitute for eggs which a persevering bagman had forced into his stock, he would answer that 'when you did not put eggs into a pudding it was difficult to taste them there'; and when he was asked if his 'real Mocha coffee' was real Mocha, he would say grimly, 'as understood in small shops'. The way to wealth was not by this route.

patronage: regular custom, but see also p56 meaning superiority
genteelest: highest class

One summer day, when the big brick house opposite was reflecting the oppressive sun's heat into the shop, and nobody was present but husband and wife, Joanna looked across at Emily's door, where a wealthy visitor's carriage had drawn up. Traces of **patronage** had been visible in Emily's manner of late.

'Shadrach, the truth is, you are not a businessman,' his wife sadly murmured. 'You were not brought up to shopkeeping, and it is impossible for a man to make a fortune at an occupation he has jumped into, as you did into this.'

Jolliffe agreed with her, in this as in everything else. 'Not that I care a rope's end about making a fortune,' he said cheerfully. 'I am happy enough, and we can rub on somehow.'

She looked again at the great house through the screen of bottled pickles.

'Rub on – yes,' she said bitterly. 'But see how well off Emmy Lester is, who used to be so poor! Her boys will go to College, no doubt; and think of yours – obliged to go to the Parish School!'

Shadrach's thoughts had flown to Emily.

'Nobody,' he said good-humouredly, 'ever did Emily a better turn than you did, Joanna, when you warned her off me and put an end to that little simpering nonsense between us, so as to leave it in her power to say "Aye" to Lester when he came along.'

This almost maddened her.

'Don't speak of bygones!' she implored, in stern sadness. 'But think, for the boys' and my sake, if not for your own, what are we to do to get richer?'

'Well,' he said, becoming serious, 'to tell the truth, I have always felt myself unfit for this business, though I've never liked to say so. I seem to want more room for sprawling; a more open space to strike out in than here among friends and neighbours. I could get rich as well as any man, if I tried my own way.'

'I wish you would! What is your way?'

'To go to sea again.'

She had been the very one to keep him at home, hating the semi-widowed existence of sailors' wives. But her ambition checked her instincts now, and she said:

'Do you think success really lies that way?'

'I am sure it lies in no other.'

'Do you want to go, Shadrach?'

'Not for the pleasure of it, I can tell 'ee. There's no such pleasure at sea, Joanna, as I can find in my back parlour here. To speak honest, I have no love for the **brine**. I never had much. But if it comes to a question of a fortune for you and the lads, it is another thing. That's the only way to it for one born and bred a seafarer as I.'

'Would it take long to earn?'

'Well, that depends; perhaps not.'

The next morning Shadrach pulled from a chest of drawers the nautical jacket he had worn during the first months of his return, brushed out the moths, donned it, and walked down to the quay. The port still did a fair business in the Newfoundland trade, though not so much as formerly.

It was not long after this that he invested all he possessed in purchasing a part-ownership in a brig, of which he was appointed captain. A few months were passed in coast-trading, during which interval Shadrach wore off the land-rust that had accumulated upon him in his grocery phase; and in the spring the brig sailed for Newfoundland.

Joanna lived on at home with her sons, who were now growing up into strong lads, and occupying themselves in various ways about the harbour and quay.

'Never mind, let them work a little,' their fond mother said to herself. 'Our necessities compel it now, but when Shadrach comes home they will be only seventeen and eighteen, and they shall be removed from the port, and their education thoroughly taken in hand by a tutor; and with the money they'll have they will perhaps be as near to gentlemen as Emmy Lester's precious two, with their algebra and their Latin!'

---

brine: sea

The date for Shadrach's return drew near and arrived, and
he did not appear. Joanna was assured that there was no cause
for anxiety, sailing-ships being so uncertain in their coming;
which assurance proved to be well grounded, for late one wet
evening, about a month after the calculated time, the ship was
announced as at hand, and presently the slip-slop step of
Shadrach as the sailor sounded in the passage, and he entered.
The boys had gone out and had missed him, and Joanna was
sitting alone.

As soon as the first emotion of reunion between the couple
had passed, Jolliffe explained the delay as owing to a small
speculative contract, which had produced good results.

'I was determined not to disappoint 'ee,' he said; 'and I think
you'll **own** that I haven't!'

With this he pulled out an enormous canvas bag, full and
rotund as the money-bag of the giant whom Jack slew, untied it,
and shook the contents out onto her lap as she sat in her low
chair by the fire. A mass of sovereigns and guineas (there were
guineas on the earth in those days) fell into her lap with a
sudden thud, weighing down her gown to the floor.

'There!' said Shadrach complacently. 'I told 'ee, dear, I'd do
it; and have I done it or no?'

Somehow her face, after the first excitement of possession,
did not retain its glory.

'It is a lot of gold, indeed,' she said. 'And – is this *all*?'

'All? Why, dear Joanna, do you know you can count to three-
hundred in that heap? It is a fortune!'

'Yes – yes. A fortune – judged by sea; but judged by land –'

However, she banished considerations of the money **for the
nonce**. Soon the boys came in, and next Sunday Shadrach
returned thanks to God – this time by the more ordinary
channel of the italics in the General Thanksgiving. But a few
days after, when the question of investing the money arose, he
remarked that she did not seem so satisfied as he had hoped.

'Well, you see, Shadrach,' she answered, '*we* count by
hundreds; *they* count by thousands' (nodding towards the

---

own: admit
for the nonce: for the time being

other side of the Street). 'They have set up a carriage and pair since you left.'

'O, have they?'

'My dear Shadrach, you don't know how the world moves. However, we'll do the best we can with it. But they are rich, and we are poor still!'

The greater part of a year was desultorily spent. She moved sadly about the house and shop, and the boys were still occupying themselves in and around the harbour.

'Joanna,' he said, one day, 'I see by your movements that it is still not enough.'

'It is not enough,' said she. 'My boys will have to live by steering the ships that the Lesters own; and I was once above her!'

Jolliffe was not an argumentative man, and he only murmured that he thought he would make another voyage. He meditated for several days, and coming home from the quay one afternoon said suddenly:

'I could do it for 'ee, dear, in one more trip, for certain, if – if –'

'Do what, Shadrach?'

'Enable 'ee to count by thousands instead of hundreds.'

'If what?'

'If I might take the boys.'

She turned pale.

'Don't say that, Shadrach,' she answered hastily.

'Why?'

'I don't like to hear it! There's danger at sea. I want them to be something genteel, and no danger to them. I couldn't let them risk their lives at sea. O, I couldn't ever, ever!'

'Very well, dear, it shan't be done.'

Next day, after a silence, she asked a question:

'If they were to go with you it would make a great deal of difference, I suppose, to the profit?'

' 'Twould treble what I should get from the venture single-handed. Under my eye they would be as good as two more of myself.'

Later on she said: 'Tell me more about this.'

'Well, the boys are almost as clever as master-mariners in handling a craft, upon my life! There isn't a more cranky place in the Northern Seas than about the sandbanks of this harbour, and they've practised here from their infancy. And they are so steady. I couldn't get their steadiness and their trustworthiness in half a dozen men twice their age.'

'And is it *very* dangerous at sea; now, too, there are rumours of war?' she asked uneasily.

'O, well, there be risks. Still . . .'

The idea grew and magnified, and the mother's heart was crushed and stifled by it. Emmy was growing *too* patronising; it could not be borne. Shadrach's wife could not help nagging him about their comparative poverty. The young men, amiable as their father, when spoken to on the subject of a voyage of enterprise, were quite willing to embark; and though they, like their father, had no great love for the sea, they became quite enthusiastic when the proposal was detailed.

Everything now hung upon their mother's assent. She withheld it long, but at last gave the word: the young men might accompany their father. Shadrach was unusually cheerful about it: Heaven had preserved him hitherto, and he had uttered his thanks. God would not forsake those who were faithful to him.

All that the Jolliffes possessed in the world was put into the enterprise. The grocery stock was pared down to the least that possibly could afford a bare sustenance to Joanna during the absence, which was to last through the usual '**New-f'nland spell**'. How she would endure the weary time she hardly knew, for the boys had been with her formerly; but she nerved herself for the trial.

The ship was laden with boots and shoes, ready-made clothing, fishing-tackle, butter, cheese, cordage, sailcloth, and many other commodities; and was to bring back oil, furs, skins, fish, cranberries, and what else came to hand. But much speculative trading to other ports was to be undertaken between the voyages out and homeward, and thereby much money made.

New-f'nland spell: trading voyage to Newfoundland

THREE

The brig sailed on a Monday morning in spring, but Joanna did not witness its departure. She could not bear the sight that she had been the means of bringing about. Knowing this, her husband told her overnight that they were to sail some time before noon next day; hence when, awakening at five the next morning, she heard them bustling about downstairs, she did not hasten to descend, but lay trying to nerve herself for the parting, imagining they would leave about nine, as her husband had done on his previous voyage. When she did descend she beheld words chalked upon the sloping face of the bureau; but no husband or sons. In the hastily-scrawled lines Shadrach said they had gone off thus not to pain her by a leave-taking; and the sons had chalked under his words: 'Goodbye, mother!'

She rushed to the quay and looked down the harbour towards the blue rim of the sea, but she could only see the masts and bulging sails of the *Joanna*; no human figures. ' 'Tis I have sent them!' she said wildly, and burst into tears. In the house the chalked 'Goodbye' nearly broke her heart. But when she had re-entered the front room, and looked across at Emily's, a gleam of triumph lit her thin face at her anticipated release from the **thraldom of subservience**.

To do Emily Lester justice, her assumption of superiority was mainly a figment of Joanna's brain. That the circumstances of the merchant's wife were more luxurious than Joanna's, the former could not conceal; though whenever the two met, which was not very often now, Emily endeavoured to subdue the difference by every means in her power.

The first summer lapsed away; and Joanna meagrely maintained herself by the shop, which now consisted of little more than a window and a counter. Emily was, in truth, her only large customer; and Mrs Lester's kindly readiness to buy anything and everything without questioning the quality had a sting of bitterness in it, for it was the uncritical attitude of a patron, and almost of a donor. The long dreary winter moved

---

thraldom of subservience: inescapable feeling of inferiority

on; the face of the bureau had been turned to the wall to protect the chalked words of farewell, for Joanna could never bring herself to rub them out; and she often glanced at them with wet eyes. Emily's handsome boys came home for the Christmas holidays; the University was talked of for them; and still Joanna subsisted as it were with held breath, like a person submerged. Only one summer more, and the 'spell' would end. Towards the close of the time Emily called on her **quondam** friend. She had heard that Joanna began to feel anxious; she had received no letter from husband or sons for some months. Emily's silks rustled arrogantly when, in response to Joanna's almost dumb invitation, she squeezed through the opening of the counter and into the parlour behind the shop.

'*You* are all success, and *I* am all the other way!' said Joanna.

'But why do you think so?' said Emily. 'They are to bring back a fortune, I hear.'

'Ah, will they come? The doubt is more than a woman can bear. All three in one ship – think of that! And I have not heard of them for months!'

'But the time is not up. You should not meet misfortune half-way.'

'Nothing will repay me for the grief of their absence!'

'Then why did you let them go? You were doing fairly well.'

'I *made* them go!' she said, turning vehemently upon Emily. 'And I'll tell you why! I could not bear that we should be only muddling on, and you so rich and thriving! Now I have told you, and you may hate me if you will!'

'I shall never hate you, Joanna.'

And she proved the truth of her words afterwards. The end of autumn came, and the brig should have been in port; but nothing like the *Joanna* appeared in the channel between the sands. It was now really time to be uneasy. Joanna Jolliffe sat by the fire, and every gust of wind caused her a cold thrill. She had always feared and detested the sea; to her it was a treacherous, restless, slimy creature, glorying in the griefs of women. 'Still,' she said, 'they *must* come!'

---

quondam: former

She recalled to her mind that Shadrach had said before starting that if they returned safe and sound, with success crowning their enterprise, he would go as he had gone after his shipwreck, and kneel with his sons in the church, and offer sincere thanks for their deliverance. She went to church regularly morning and afternoon, and sat in the most forward pew, nearest the chancel-step. Her eyes were mostly fixed on that step, where Shadrach had knelt in the bloom of his young manhood: she knew to an inch the spot which his knees had pressed twenty winters before; his outline as he had knelt, his hat on the step beside him. God was good. Surely her husband must kneel there again: a son on each side as he had said; George just here, Jim just there. By long watching the spot as she worshipped became as if she saw the three returned ones there kneeling; the two slim outlines of her boys, the more bulky form between them; their hands clasped, their heads shaped against the eastern wall. The fancy grew almost to an hallucination: she could never turn her worn eyes to the step without seeing them there.

Nevertheless, they did not come. Heaven was merciful, but it was not yet pleased to relieve her soul. This was her **purgation** for the sin of making them the slaves of her ambition. But it became more than purgation soon, and her mood approached despair. Months had passed since the brig had been due, but it had not returned.

Joanna was always hearing or seeing evidences of their arrival. When on the hill behind the port, whence a view of the open Channel could be obtained, she felt sure that a little speck on the horizon, breaking the eternally level waste of waters southward, was the truck of the *Joanna*'s mainmast. Or when indoors, a shout of excitement of any kind at the corner of the Town Cellar, where the High Street joined the Quay, caused her to spring to her feet and cry: ' 'Tis they!'

But it was not. The visionary forms knelt every Sunday afternoon on the chancel-step, but not the real. Her shop had, as it were, eaten itself hollow. In the apathy which had resulted

purgation: penance

from her loneliness and grief she had ceased to take in the smallest supplies, and thus had sent away her last customer.

In this strait Emily Lester tried by every means in her power to aid the afflicted woman; but she met with constant repulses.

'I don't like you! I can't bear to see you!' Joanna would whisper hoarsely when Emily came to her and made advances.

'But I want to help and soothe you, Joanna,' Emily would say.

'You are a lady, with a rich husband and fine sons! What can you want with a bereaved crone like me!'

'Joanna, I want this: I want you to come and live in my house, and not stay alone in this dismal place any longer.'

'And suppose they come and don't find me at home? You wish to separate me and mine! No, I'll stay here. I don't like you, and I can't thank you, whatever kindness you do me!'

However, as time went on Joanna could not afford to pay the rent of the shop and house without an income. She was assured that all hope of the return of Shadrach and his sons was vain, and she reluctantly consented to accept the **asylum** of the Lesters' house. Here she was allotted a room of her own on the second floor, and went and came as she chose, without contact with the family. Her hair greyed and whitened, deep lines channeled her forehead, and her form grew gaunt and stooping. But she still expected the lost ones, and when she met Emily on the staircase she would say morosely: 'I know why you've got me here! They'll come, and be disappointed at not finding me at home, and perhaps go away again; and then you'll be revenged for my taking Shadrach away from 'ee!'

Emily Lester bore these reproaches from the grief-stricken soul. She was sure – all the people of Havenpool were sure – that Shadrach and his sons had gone to the bottom. For years the vessel had been given up as lost. Nevertheless, when awakened at night by any noise, Joanna would rise from bed and glance at the shop opposite by the light from the flickering lamp, to make sure it was not they.

It was a damp and dark December night, six years after the departure of the brig *Joanna*. The wind was from the sea, and

---

asylum: shelter

brought up a fishy mist which mopped the face like a moist flannel. Joanna had prayed her usual prayer for the absent ones with more fervour and confidence than she had felt for months, and had fallen asleep about eleven. It must have been between one and two when she suddenly started up. She had certainly heard steps in the street, and the voices of Shadrach and her sons calling at the door of the grocery shop. She sprang out of bed, and, hardly knowing what clothing she dragged on herself, hastened down Emily's large and carpeted staircase, put the candle on the hall-table, unfastened the bolts and chain, and stepped into the street. The mist, blowing up the street from the Quay, hindered her seeing the shop, although it was so near; but she had crossed to it in a moment. How was it? Nobody stood there. The wretched woman walked wildly up and down with her bare feet – there was not a soul. She returned and knocked with her all might at the door which had once been her own – they might have been admitted for the night, unwilling to disturb her till the morning. It was not till several minutes had elapsed that the young man who now kept the shop looked out of an upper window, and saw the skeleton of something human standing below half-dressed.

'Has anybody come?' asked the form.

'O, Mrs Jolliffe, I didn't know it was you,' said the young man kindly, for he was aware how her baseless expectations moved her. 'No; nobody has come.'

Non-fiction passages linked to
To Please His Wife (1891)

Shopkeeping in a small town around 1890

a One likely reason why the Jolliffes' shop did not thrive was the customers' unwillingness, or inability, to pay:

Credit played an important part in the shopkeeper's trade. Squires, farmers and other tradesmen rarely paid cash, buying instead on account and settling once every month or six weeks. It was not uncommon to have to wait a year or more for payment.

It was the same with the poor, except that they did not have unsettled accounts, they simply had debt. Labourers, smallholders and small-time tradesmen found it easy to slip into debt with the shopkeeper, even on quite a small purchase of tea, sugar, starch and soap. Once incurred, it could take years for debts to be cleared. There was a smallholder who had built up a debt with the same shop during 1895 of £9 10s. He made a number of small occasional payments during succeeding years, resorting to barter on occasions – his potato crop of 1896 went to the shopkeeper. His debt was not finally cleared until 1915.

Sadie Ward, 1986

b Running their grocer's shop would have meant hard work and long hours for Joanna and Shadrach:

> The grocer of the nineteenth century bought wholesale consignments – sacks of flour and oatmeal, barrels of vinegar and dried fruit, chests of tea. Sugar was supplied as a solid cone of 'loaf sugar' which had to be cut into the ounces and pounds which customers wanted to buy – a laborious task. Salt also arrived in a large block, and soap came as a slab about eighteen inches long to be sliced into one-pound bars. Dried fruit had to be cleaned by being rubbed through sieves. Bacon was sliced by hand, coffee was ground, and tea blended.

Jonathan Brown, 1990

A middle-class lady's life around 1890

a Emily, married to a rich merchant, would have found her daily life in striking contrast to Joanna's:

> Even when I first married it would never have occurred to me that I could possibly cook myself, or that I could care for my baby alone. It was not that I was too proud to work – it was simply that I had not the faintest idea how to begin to run a house by myself, and would not have thought that I could do it.
>
> Ladies were ladies in those days; they did not do things themselves, they told other people what to do and how to do it.

Gwen Ravaret, remembering the 1890s

b In their 'genteel' house, Emily's children would have been brought up quite differently from Joanna's:

Working-class mothers knew their job: to feed, clothe, house their children and teach them to behave. On the other hand, in the middle and upper classes the tasks of motherhood were largely delegated to a nanny or nursemaid, or both. Mothers convinced themselves that nanny would do a better job as she was less emotionally involved – although, quite often, it was the mother who remained the more detached of the two. 'Nanny was my life. She was my authority,' explained Mary Lutyens. 'Mother was a goddess. It was unthinkable that a goddess should bath me.'

The children's world revolved around the nursery, tucked away on the top floor far from their parents. They had all their meals in the nursery, their lessons in the nursery, and their mother visited them in the nursery after tea to read to them. As a child in the 1890s, Mary Lutyens was much closer to Nanny Sleath than to her mother. Mary 'couldn't have borne the shame' if her mother had seen her without clothes. When, at fifteen, she was sick in front of her, she was 'terribly ashamed' and amazed that her mother could hold her head without appearing to be disgusted.

Angela Holdsworth, 1988

A Victorian wife's place within marriage

Joanna is the decision-maker in her marriage. A wife taking control was seen by most Victorians, including the Queen herself, as a dangerous reversal of the natural order:

The Queen is most anxious to enlist every one who can speak or write to join in checking this mad, wicked folly of 'Women's Rights', with all its attendant horrors, on which her poor feeble sex is bent, forgetting every sense of womanly feeling and propriety … God created men and women different – then let them remain each in their own position.

Queen Victoria, 1870

The Adventure of the Beryl Coronet
Arthur Conan Doyle

'Holmes,' said I as I stood one morning in our bow-window looking down the street, 'here is a madman coming along. It seems rather sad that his relatives should allow him to come out alone.'

My friend rose lazily from his armchair and stood with his hands in the pockets of his dressing-gown, looking over my shoulder. It was a bright, crisp February morning, and the snow of the day before still lay deep upon the ground, shimmering brightly in the wintry sun. Down the centre of Baker Street it had been ploughed into a brown crumbly band by the traffic, but at either side and on the heaped-up edges of the foot-paths it still lay as white as when it fell. The grey pavement had been cleaned and scraped, but was still dangerously slippery, so that there were fewer passengers than usual. Indeed, from the direction of the Metropolitan Station no one was coming save the single gentleman whose eccentric conduct had drawn my attention.

He was a man of about fifty, tall, portly, and imposing, with a massive, strongly marked face and a commanding figure. He was dressed in a sombre yet rich style, in black frock-coat, shining hat, neat brown gaiters, and well-cut pearl-grey trousers. Yet his actions were in absurd contrast to the dignity of his dress and features, for he was running hard, with occasional little springs, such as a weary man gives who is little accustomed to set any tax upon his legs. As he ran he jerked his hands up and down, waggled his head, and writhed his face into the most extraordinary contortions.

'What on earth can be the matter with him?' I asked. 'He is looking up at the numbers of the houses.'

'I believe that he is coming here,' said Holmes, rubbing his hands.

'Here?'

'Yes; I rather think he is coming to consult me professionally. I think that I recognise the symptoms. Ha! did I not tell you?' As he spoke, the man, puffing and blowing, rushed at our door and pulled at our bell until the whole house resounded with the clanging.

A few moments later he was in our room, still puffing, still gesticulating, but with so fixed a look of grief and despair in his eyes that our smiles were turned in an instant to horror and pity. For a while he could not get his words out, but swayed his body and plucked at his hair like one who had been driven to the extreme limits of his reason. Then, suddenly springing to his feet, he beat his head against the wall with such force that we both rushed upon him and tore him away to the centre of the room. Sherlock Holmes pushed him down into the easy-chair and, sitting beside him, patted his hand and chatted with him in the easy, soothing tones which he knew so well how to employ.

'You have come to me to tell your story, have you not?' said he. 'You are fatigued with your haste. Pray wait until you have recovered yourself, and then I shall be most happy to look into any little problem which you may submit to me.'

The man sat for a minute or more with a heaving chest, fighting against his emotion. Then he passed his handkerchief over his brow, set his lips tight, and turned his face towards us.

'No doubt you think me mad?' said he.

'I see that you have had some great trouble,' responded Holmes.

'God knows I have! – a trouble which is enough to **unseat my reason**, so sudden and so terrible is it. Public disgrace I might have faced, although I am a man whose character has never yet borne a strain. Private affliction also is the lot of every man; but the two coming together, and in so frightful a form, have been enough to shake my very soul. Besides, it is not I alone. The very noblest in the land may suffer unless some way be found out of this horrible affair.'

'Pray compose yourself, sir,' said Holmes, 'and let me have a clear account of who you are and what it is that has befallen you.'

---

unseat my reason: drive me insane

'My name,' answered our visitor, 'is probably familiar to your ears. I am Alexander Holder, of the banking firm Holder & Stevenson, of Threadneedle Street.'

The name was indeed well known to us as belonging to the senior partner in the second largest private banking concern in the City of London. What could have happened, then, to bring one of the foremost citizens of London to this most pitiable pass? We waited, all curiosity, until with another effort he braced himself to tell his story.

'I feel that time is of value,' said he; 'that is why I hastened here when the police inspector suggested that I should secure your cooperation. I came to Baker Street by the Underground and hurried from there on foot, for the cabs go slowly through this snow. That is why I was so out of breath, for I am a man who takes very little exercise. I feel better now, and I will put the facts before you as shortly and yet as clearly as I can.

'It is, of course, well known to you that in a successful banking business as much depends upon our being able to find **remunerative** investments for our funds as upon our increasing our connection and the number of our depositors. One of our most lucrative means of laying out money is in the shape of loans, where the security is **unimpeachable**. We have done a good deal in this direction during the last few years, and there are many noble families to whom we have advanced large sums upon the security of their pictures, libraries, or plate.

'Yesterday morning I was seated in my office at the bank when a card was brought in to me by one of the clerks. I started when I saw the name, for it was that of none other than – well, perhaps even to you I had better say no more than that it was a name which is a household word all over the earth – one of the highest, noblest, most exalted names in England. I was overwhelmed by the honour and attempted, when he entered, to say so, but he plunged at once into business with the air of a man who wishes to hurry quickly through a disagreeable task.

'"Mr Holder," said he, "I have been informed that you are in the habit of advancing money."

remunerative: profitable
unimpeachable: absolutely reliable

'"The firm does so when the security is good," I answered.

'"It is absolutely essential to me," said he, "that I should have £50,000 at once. I could, of course, borrow so trifling a sum ten times over from my friends, but I much prefer to make it a matter of business and to carry out that business myself. In my position you can readily understand that it is unwise to place one's self under obligations."

'"For how long, may I ask, do you want this sum?" I said.

'"Next Monday I have a large sum due to me, and I shall then most certainly repay what you advance, with whatever interest you think it right to charge. But it is very essential to me that the money should be paid at once."

'"I should be happy to advance it without further **parley** from my own private purse," said I, "were it not that the strain would be rather more than it could bear. If, on the other hand, I am to do it in the name of the firm, then in justice to my partner I must insist that, even in your case, every businesslike precaution should be taken."

'"I should much prefer to have it so," said he, raising up a square, black morocco case which he had laid beside the chair. "You have doubtless heard of the Beryl Coronet?"

'"One of the most precious public possessions of the empire," said I.

'"Precisely." He opened the case, and there, imbedded in soft, flesh-coloured velvet, lay the magnificent piece of jewellery which he had named. "There are thirty-nine enormous **beryls**," said he, "and the price of the gold chasing is incalculable. The lowest estimate would put the worth of the coronet at double the sum which I have asked. I am prepared to leave it with you as my security."

'I took the precious case into my hands and looked in some perplexity from it to my illustrious client.

'"You doubt its value?" he asked.

'"Not at all. I only doubt – "

'"The propriety of my leaving it. You may set your mind at rest about that. I should not dream of doing so were it not

---

parley: discussion
beryls: pale green jewels (gems)

absolutely certain that I should be able in four days to reclaim it. It is a pure matter of form. Is the security sufficient?"

'"Ample."

'"You understand, Mr Holder, that I am giving you a strong proof of the confidence which I have in you, founded upon all that I have heard of you. I rely upon you not only to be discreet and to refrain from all gossip upon the matter but, above all, to preserve this coronet with every possible precaution because I need not say that a great public scandal would be caused if any harm were to befall it. Any injury to it would be almost as serious as its complete loss, for there are no beryls in the world to match these, and it would be impossible to replace them. I leave it with you, however, with every confidence, and I shall call for it in person on Monday morning."

'Seeing that my client was anxious to leave, I said no more; but, calling for my cashier, I ordered him to pay over fifty £1000 notes. When I was alone once more, however, with the precious case lying upon the table in front of me, I could not but think with some misgivings of the immense responsibility which it entailed upon me. There could be no doubt that, as it was a national possession, a horrible scandal would ensue if any misfortune should occur to it. I already regretted having ever consented to take charge of it. However, it was too late to alter the matter now, so I locked it up in my private safe and turned once more to my work.

'When the evening came I felt that it would be an **imprudence** to leave so precious a thing in the office behind me. Bankers' safes had been forced before now, and why should not mine be? If so, how terrible would be the position in which I should find myself! I determined, therefore, that for the next few days I would always carry the case backward and forward with me, so that it might never be really out of my reach. With this intention, I called a cab and drove out to my house at Streatham, carrying the jewel with me. I did not breathe freely until I had taken it upstairs and locked it in the bureau of my dressing-room.

---

imprudence: risk

'And now a word as to my household, Mr Holmes, for I wish you to thoroughly understand the situation. My groom and my page sleep out of the house, and may be set aside altogether. I have three maid-servants who have been with me a number of years and whose absolute reliability is quite above suspicion. Another, Lucy Parr, the second waiting-maid, has only been in my service a few months. She came with an excellent character, however, and has always given me satisfaction. She is a very pretty girl and has attracted admirers who have occasionally hung about the place. That is the only drawback which we have found to her, but we believe her to be a thoroughly good girl in every way.

'So much for the servants. My family itself is so small that it will not take me long to describe it. I am a widower and have an only son, Arthur. He has been a disappointment to me, Mr Holmes – a grievous disappointment. I have no doubt that I am myself to blame. People tell me that I have spoiled him. Very likely I have. When my dear wife died I felt that he was all I had to love. I could not bear to see the smile fade even for a moment from his face. I have never denied him a wish. Perhaps it would have been better for both of us had I been sterner, but I meant it for the best.

'It was naturally my intention that he should succeed me in my business, but he was not of a business turn. He was wild, wayward, and, to speak the truth, I could not trust him in the handling of large sums of money. When he was young he became a member of an aristocratic club, and there, having charming manners, he was soon the intimate of a number of men with long purses and expensive habits. He learned to play heavily at cards and to squander money on **the turf**, until he had again and again to come to me and implore me to give him an advance upon his allowance, that he might settle his debts of honour. He tried more than once to break away from the dangerous company which he was keeping, but each time the influence of his friend, Sir George Burnwell, was enough to draw him back again.

the turf: horse-racing

'And, indeed, I could not wonder that such a man as Sir George Burnwell should gain an influence over him, for he has frequently brought him to my house, and I have found myself that I could hardly resist the fascination of his manner. He is older than Arthur, a man of the world to his finger-tips, one who has been everywhere, seen everything, a brilliant talker, and a man of great personal beauty. Yet when I think of him in cold blood, far away from the glamour of his presence, I am convinced from his cynical speech and the look which I have caught in his eyes that he is one who should be deeply distrusted. So I think, and so, too, thinks my little Mary, who has a woman's quick insight into character.

'And now there is only she to be described. She is my niece; but when my brother died five years ago and left her alone in the world I adopted her, and have looked upon her ever since as my daughter. She is a sunbeam in my house – sweet, loving, beautiful, a wonderful manager and housekeeper, yet as tender and quiet and gentle as a woman could be. She is my right hand. I do not know what I could do without her. In only one matter has she ever gone against my wishes. Twice my boy has asked her to marry him, for he loves her devotedly, but each time she has refused him. I think that if anyone could have drawn him into the right path it would have been she, and that his marriage might have changed his whole life; but now, alas! it is too late – forever too late!

'Now, Mr Holmes, you know the people who live under my roof, and I shall continue with my miserable story.

'When we were taking coffee in the drawing-room that night after dinner, I told Arthur and Mary my experience, and of the precious treasure which we had under our roof, suppressing only the name of the client. Lucy Parr, who had brought in the coffee, had, I am sure, left the room; but I cannot swear that the door was closed. Mary and Arthur were much interested and wished to see the famous coronet, but I thought it better not to disturb it.

'"Where have you put it?" asked Arthur.

'"In my own bureau."

'"Well, I hope to goodness the house won't be burgled during the night," said he.

'"It is locked up," I answered.

'"Oh, any old key will fit that bureau. When I was a youngster I have opened it myself with the key of the box-room cupboard."

'He often had a wild way of talking, so that I thought little of what he said. He followed me to my room, however, that night with a very grave face.

'"Look here, dad," said he with his eyes cast down, "can you let me have £200?"

'"No, I cannot!" I answered sharply. "I have been far too generous with you in money matters."

'"You have been very kind," said he, "but I must have this money, or else I can never show my face inside the club again."

'"And a very good thing, too!" I cried.

'"Yes, but you would not have me leave it a dishonoured man," said he. "I could not bear the disgrace. I must raise the money in some way, and if you will not let me have it, then I must try other means."

'I was very angry, for this was the third demand during the month. "You shall not have a farthing from me," I cried, on which he bowed and left the room without another word.

'When he was gone I unlocked my bureau, made sure that my treasure was safe, and locked it again. Then I started to go round the house to see that all was secure – a duty which I usually leave to Mary but which I thought it well to perform myself that night. As I came down the stairs I saw Mary herself at the side window of the hall, which she closed and fastened as I approached.

'"Tell me, dad," said she, looking, I thought, a little disturbed, "did you give Lucy, the maid, leave to go out to-night?"

'"Certainly not."

'"She came in just now by the back door. I have no doubt that she has only been to the side gate to see someone, but I think that it is hardly safe and should be stopped."

'"You must speak to her in the morning, or I will if you prefer it. Are you sure that everything is fastened?"

'"Quite sure, dad."

'"Then, good-night." I kissed her and went up to my bedroom again, where I was soon asleep.

'I am endeavouring to tell you everything, Mr Holmes, which may have any bearing upon the case, but I beg that you will question me upon any point which I do not make clear.'

'On the contrary, your statement is singularly lucid.'

'I come to a part of my story now in which I should wish to be particularly so. I am not a very heavy sleeper, and the anxiety in my mind tended, no doubt, to make me even less so than usual. About two in the morning, then, I was awakened by some sound in the house. It had ceased ere I was wide awake, but it had left an impression behind it as though a window had gently closed somewhere. I lay listening with all my ears. Suddenly, to my horror, there was a distant sound of footsteps moving softly in the next room. I slipped out of bed, all palpitating with fear, and peeped round the corner of my dressing-room door.

'"Arthur!" I screamed, "you villain! you thief! How dare you touch that coronet?"

'The gas was half up, as I had left it, and my unhappy boy, dressed only in his shirt and trousers, was standing beside the light, holding the coronet in his hands. He appeared to be wrenching at it, or bending it with all his strength. At my cry he dropped it from his grasp and turned as pale as death. I snatched it up and examined it. One of the gold corners, with three of the beryls in it, was missing.

'"You blackguard!" I shouted, beside myself with rage. "You have destroyed it! You have dishonoured me forever! Where are the jewels which you have stolen?"

'"Stolen!" he cried.

'"Yes, thief!" I roared, shaking him by the shoulder.

'"There are none missing. There cannot be any missing," said he.

'"There are three missing. And you know where they are. Must I call you a liar as well as a thief? Did I not see you trying to tear off another piece?"

'"You have called me names enough," said he; "I will not stand it any longer. I shall not say another word about this business, since you have chosen to insult me. I will leave your house in the morning and make my own way in the world."

'"You shall leave it in the hands of the police!" I cried, half-mad with grief and rage. "I shall have this matter probed to the bottom."

'"You shall learn nothing from me," said he with a passion such as I should not have thought was in his nature. "If you choose to call the police, let the police find what they can."

'By this time the whole house was astir, for I had raised my voice in my anger. Mary was the first to rush into my room, and, at the sight of the coronet and of Arthur's face, she read the whole story and, with a scream, fell down senseless on the ground. I sent the house-maid for the police and put the investigation into their hands at once. When the inspector and a constable entered the house, Arthur, who had stood sullenly with his arms folded, asked me whether it was my intention to charge him with theft. I answered that it had ceased to be a private matter, but had become a public one, since the ruined coronet was national property. I was determined that the law should have its way in everything.

'"At least," said he, "you will not have me arrested at once. It would be to your advantage as well as mine if I might leave the house for five minutes."

'"That you may get away, or perhaps that you may conceal what you have stolen," said I. And then, realising the dreadful position in which I was placed, I implored him to remember that not only my honour but that of one who was far greater than I was at stake; and that he threatened to raise a scandal which would convulse the nation. He might avert it all if he would but tell me what he had done with the three missing stones.

'"You may as well face the matter," said I; "you have been caught in the act, and no confession could make your guilt more **heinous**. If you but make such reparation as is in your power, by telling us where the beryls are, all shall be forgiven and forgotten."

---

heinous: dreadful

'"Keep your forgiveness for those who ask for it," he answered, turning away from me with a sneer. I saw that he was too hardened for any words of mine to influence him. There was but one way for it. I called in the inspector and gave him into custody. A search was made at once not only of his person but of his room and of every portion of the house where he could possibly have concealed the gems; but no trace of them could be found, nor would the wretched boy open his mouth for all our persuasions and our threats. This morning he was removed to a cell, and I, after going through all the police formalities, have hurried round to you to implore you to use your skill in unravelling the matter. The police have openly confessed that they can at present make nothing of it. You may go to any expense which you think necessary. I have already offered a reward of £1000. My God, what shall I do! I have lost my honour, my gems, and my son in one night. Oh, what shall I do!'

He put a hand on either side of his head and rocked himself to and fro, droning to himself like a child whose grief has got beyond words.

Sherlock Holmes sat silent for some few minutes, with his brows knitted and his eyes fixed upon the fire.

'Do you receive much company?' he asked.

'None save my partner with his family and an occasional friend of Arthur's. Sir George Burnwell has been several times lately. No one else, I think.'

'Do you go out much in society?'

'Arthur does. Mary and I stay at home. We neither of us care for it.'

'That is unusual in a young girl.'

'She is of a quiet nature. Besides, she is not so very young. She is four-and-twenty.'

'This matter, from what you say, seems to have been a shock to her also.'

'Terrible! She is even more affected than I.'

'You have neither of you any doubt as to your son's guilt?'

'How can we have when I saw him with my open eyes with the coronet in his hands.'

'I hardly consider that a conclusive proof. Was the remainder of the coronet at all injured?'

'Yes, it was twisted.'

'Do you not think then, that he might have been trying to straighten it?'

'God bless you! You are doing what you can for him and for me. But it is too heavy a task. What was he doing there at all? If his purpose were innocent, why did he not say so?'

'Precisely. And if it were guilty, why did he not invent a lie? His silence appears to me to cut both ways. There are several singular points about the case. What did the police think of the noise which awoke you from your sleep?'

'They considered that it might be caused by Arthur's closing his bedroom door.'

'A likely story! As if a man bent on **felony** would slam his door so as to wake a household. What did they say, then, of the disappearance of these gems?'

'They are still sounding the planking and probing the furniture in the hope of finding them.'

'Have they thought of looking outside the house?'

'Yes, they have shown extraordinary energy. The whole garden has already been minutely examined.'

'Now, my dear sir,' said Holmes, 'is it not obvious to you that this matter really strikes very much deeper than either you or the police were at first inclined to think? It appeared to you to be a simple case; to me it seems exceedingly complex. Consider what is involved by your theory. You suppose that your son came down from his bed, went, at great risk, to your dressing-room, opened your bureau, took out the coronet, broke off by main force a small portion of it, went off to some other place, concealed three gems out of the thirty-nine, with such skill that nobody can find them, and then returned with the other thirty-six into the room in which he exposed himself to the greatest danger of being discovered. I ask you now, is such a theory tenable?'

---

felony: serious crime

'But what other is there?' cried the banker with a gesture of despair. 'If his motives were innocent, why does he not explain them?'

'It is our task to find that out,' replied Holmes; 'so now, if you please, Mr Holder, we will set off for Streatham together, and devote an hour to glancing a little more closely into details.'

My friend insisted upon my accompanying them in their expedition, which I was eager enough to do, for my curiosity and sympathy were deeply stirred by the story to which we had listened. I confess that the guilt of the banker's son appeared to me to be as obvious as it did to his unhappy father, but still I had such faith in Holmes's judgement that I felt that there must be some grounds for hope as long as he was dissatisfied with the accepted explanation. He hardly spoke a word the whole way out to the southern suburb, but sat with his chin upon his breast and his hat drawn over his eyes, sunk in the deepest thought. Our client appeared to have taken fresh heart at the little glimpse of hope which had been presented to him, and he even broke in to a desultory chat with me over his business affairs. A short railway journey and a shorter walk brought us to Fairbank, the modest residence of the great financier.

Fairbank was a good-sized square house of white stone, standing back a little from the road. A double carriage-sweep, with a snow-clad lawn, stretched down in front to two large iron gates which closed the entrance. On the right side was a small wooden thicket, which led into a narrow path between two neat hedges stretching from the road to the kitchen door, and forming the tradesmen's entrance. On the left ran a lane which led to the stables, and was not itself within the grounds at all, being a public, though little used, thoroughfare. Holmes left us standing at the door and walked slowly all round the house, across the front, down the tradesmen's path, and so round the garden behind into the stable lane. So long was he that Mr Holder and I went into the dining-room and waited by the fire until he should return. We were sitting there in silence when the door opened and a young lady came in. She was rather above the middle height, slim, with dark hair and eyes, which seemed the darker against the absolute pallor of her skin. I do not think that I have ever seen such deadly paleness in a woman's face. Her lips, too, were bloodless, but her eyes were flushed with crying. As she swept silently into the room she impressed me with a greater sense of grief than the banker had done in the morning, and it was the more striking in her as she was evidently a woman of strong character, with immense capacity for self-restraint. Disregarding my presence, she went straight to her uncle and passed her hand over his head with a sweet womanly caress.

'You have given orders that Arthur should be liberated, have you not, dad?' she asked.

'No, no, my girl, the matter must be probed to the bottom.'

'But I am so sure that he is innocent. You know what woman's instincts are. I know that he has done no harm and that you will be sorry for having acted so harshly.'

'Why is he silent, then, if he is innocent?'

'Who knows? Perhaps because he was so angry that you should suspect him.'

'How could I help suspecting him, when I actually saw him with the coronet in his hand?'

'Oh, but he had only picked it up to look at it. Oh, do, do take my word for it that he is innocent. Let the matter drop and say no more. It is so dreadful to think of our dear Arthur in prison!'

'I shall never let it drop until the gems are found – never, Mary! Your affection for Arthur blinds you as to the awful consequences to me. Far from hushing the thing up, I have brought a gentleman down from London to inquire more deeply into it.'

'This gentleman?' she asked, facing round to me.

'No, his friend. He wished us to leave him alone. He is round in the stable lane now.'

'The stable lane?' She raised her dark eyebrows. 'What can he hope to find there? Ah! this, I suppose, is he. I trust, sir, that you will succeed in proving, what I feel sure is the truth, that my cousin Arthur is innocent of this crime.'

'I fully share your opinion, and I trust, with you, that we may prove it,' returned Holmes, going back to the mat to knock the snow from his shoes. 'I believe I have the honour of addressing Miss Mary Holder. Might I ask you a question or two?'

'Pray do, sir, if it may help to clear this horrible affair up.'

'You heard nothing yourself last night?'

'Nothing, until my uncle here began to speak loudly. I heard that, and I came down.'

'You shut up the windows and doors the night before. Did you fasten all the windows?'

'Yes.'

'Were they all fastened this morning?'

'Yes.'

'You have a maid who has a sweetheart? I think that you remarked to your uncle last night that she had been out to see him?'

'Yes, and she was the girl who waited in the drawing-room, and who may have heard uncle's remarks about the coronet.'

'I see. You infer that she may have gone out to tell her sweetheart, and that the two may have planned the robbery.'

'But what is the good of all these vague theories,' cried the banker impatiently, 'when I have told you that I saw Arthur with the coronet in his hands?'

'Wait a little, Mr Holder. We must come back to that. About this girl, Miss Holder. You saw her return by the kitchen door, I presume?'

'Yes; when I went to see if the door was fastened for the night I met her slipping in. I saw the man, too, in the gloom.'

'Do you know him?'

'Oh, yes! he is the green-grocer who brings our vegetables round. His name is Francis Prosper.'

'He stood,' said Holmes, 'to the left of the door – that is to say, farther up the path than is necessary to reach the door?'

'Yes, he did.'

'And he is a man with a wooden leg?'

Something like fear sprang up in the young lady's expressive black eyes. 'Why, you are like a magician,' said she. 'How do you know that?' She smiled, but there was no answering smile in Holmes's thin, eager face.

'I should be very glad now to go upstairs,' said he. 'I shall probably wish to go over the outside of the house again. Perhaps I had better take a look at the lower windows before I go up.'

He walked round swiftly from one to the other, pausing only at the large one which looked from the hall onto the stable lane. This he opened and made a very careful examination of the sill with his powerful magnifying lens. 'Now we shall go upstairs,' said he at last.

The banker's dressing-room was a plainly furnished little chamber, with a grey carpet, a large bureau, and a long mirror. Holmes went to the bureau first and looked hard at the lock.

'Which key was used to open it?' he asked.

'That which my son himself indicated – that of the cupboard of the lumber-room.'

'Have you it here?'

Sherlock Holmes took it up and opened the bureau.

'It is a noiseless lock,' said he. 'It is no wonder that it did not wake you. This case, I presume, contains the coronet. We must have a look at it.' He opened the case, and taking out the diadem he laid it upon the table. It was a magnificent specimen of the jeweller's art, and the thirty-six stones were the finest that I have ever seen. At one side of the coronet was a cracked edge, where a corner holding three gems had been torn away.

'Now, Mr Holder,' said Holmes, 'here is the corner which corresponds to that which has been so unfortunately lost. Might I beg that you will break it off.'

The banker recoiled in horror. 'I should not dream of trying,' said he.

'Then I will.' Holmes suddenly bent his strength upon it, but without result. 'I feel it give a little,' said he; 'but, though I am exceptionally strong in the fingers, it would take me all my time to break it. An ordinary man could not do it. Now, what do you think would happen if I did break it, Mr Holder? There would be a noise like a pistol shot. Do you tell me that all this happened within a few yards of your bed and that you heard nothing of it?'

'I do not know what to think. It is all dark to me.'

'But perhaps it may grow lighter as we go. What do you think, Miss Holder?'

'I confess that I still share my uncle's perplexity.'

'Your son had no shoes or slippers on when you saw him?'

'He had nothing on save only his trousers and shirt.'

'Thank you. We have certainly been favoured with extraordinary luck during this inquiry, and it will be entirely our own fault if we do not succeed in clearing the matter up. With your permission, Mr Holder, I shall now continue my investigations outside.'

He went alone, at his own request, for he explained that any unnecessary foot-marks might make his task more difficult. For an hour or more he was at work, returning at last with his feet heavy with snow and his features as inscrutable as ever.

'I think that I have seen now all that there is to see, Mr Holder,' said he; 'I can serve you best by returning to my rooms.'

'But the gems, Mr Holmes. Where are they?'

'I cannot tell.'

The banker wrung his hands. 'I shall never see them again!' he cried. 'And my son? You give me hope?'

'My opinion is in no way altered.'

'Then, for God's sake, what was this dark business which was acted in my house last night?'

'If you can call upon me at my Baker Street rooms to-morrow morning between nine and ten I shall be happy to do what I can to make it clearer. I understand that you give me **carte blanche** to act for you, provided only that I get back the gems, and that you place no limit on the sum I may draw.'

'I would give my fortune to have them back.'

'Very good. I shall look into the matter between this and then. Good-bye; it is just possible that I may have to come over here again before evening.'

It was obvious to me that my companion's mind was now made up about the case, although what his conclusions were

---

carte blanche: full permission

was more than I could even dimly imagine. Several times
during our homeward journey I endeavoured to sound him
upon the point, but he always glided away to some other topic,
until at last I gave it over in despair. It was not yet three when
we found ourselves in our rooms once more. He hurried to his
chamber, and was down again in a few minutes dressed as a
common **loafer**. With his collar turned up, his shiny, seedy coat,
his red cravat, and his worn boots, he was a perfect sample of
the class.

'I think that this should do,' said he, glancing into the glass
above the fireplace. 'I only wish that you could come with me,
Watson, but I fear that it won't do. I may be on the trail in this
matter, or I may be following a will-o'-the-wisp, but I shall soon
know which it is. I hope that I may be back in a few hours.' He
cut a slice of beef from the joint upon the sideboard,
sandwiched it between two rounds of bread, and thrusting this
rude meal into his pocket he started off upon his expedition.

I had just finished my tea when he returned, evidently in
excellent spirits, swinging an old elastic-sided boot in his hand.
He chucked it down into a corner and helped himself to a cup
of tea.

'I only looked in as I passed,' said he. 'I am going right on.'

'Where to?'

'Oh, to the other side of the West End. It may be some time
before I get back. Don't wait up for me in case I should be late.'

'How are you getting on?'

'Oh, so so. Nothing to complain of. I have been out to
Streatham since I saw you last, but I did not call at the house. It
is a very sweet little problem, and I would not have missed it for
a good deal. However, I must not sit gossiping here, but must
get these disreputable clothes off and return to my highly
respectable self.'

I could see by his manner that he had stronger reasons for
satisfaction than his words alone would imply. His eyes
twinkled, and there was even a touch of colour upon his sallow
cheeks. He hastened upstairs, and a few minutes later I heard

---

loafer: down-and-out

the slam of the hall door, which told me that he was off once more upon his congenial hunt.

I waited until midnight, but there was no sign of his return, so I retired to my room. It was no uncommon thing for him to be away for days and nights on end when he was hot upon a scent, so that his lateness caused me no surprise. I do not know at what hour he came in, but when I came down to breakfast in the morning there he was with a cup of coffee in one hand and the paper in the other, as fresh and trim as possible.

'You will excuse my beginning without you, Watson,' said he, 'but you remember that our client has rather an early appointment this morning.'

'Why, it is after nine now,' I answered. 'I should not be surprised if that were he. I thought I heard a ring.'

It was, indeed, our friend the financier. I was shocked by the change which had come over him, for his face which was naturally of a broad and massive mould, was now pinched and fallen in, while his hair seemed to me at least a shade whiter. He entered with a weariness and lethargy which was even more painful than his violence of the morning before, and he dropped heavily into the armchair which I pushed forward for him.

'I do not know what I have done to be so severely tried,' said he. 'Only two days ago I was a happy and prosperous man, without a care in the world. Now I am left to a lonely and dishonoured age. One sorrow comes close upon the heels of another. My niece, Mary, has deserted me.'

'Deserted you?'

'Yes. Her bed this morning had not been slept in, her room was empty, and a note for me lay upon the hall table. I had said to her last night, in sorrow and not in anger, that if she had married my boy all might have been well with him. Perhaps it was thoughtless of me to say so. It is to that remark that she refers in this note:

' " My dearest Uncle:
"I feel that I have brought trouble upon you, and that if I had acted differently this terrible misfortune might never have occurred. I cannot, with this thought in my mind, ever again

be happy under your roof, and I feel that I must leave you forever. Do not worry about my future, for that is provided for; and, above all, do not search for me, for it will be fruitless labour and an ill-service to me. In life or in death, I am ever

Your loving
MARY."

'What could she mean by that note, Mr Holmes? Do you think it points to suicide?'

'No, no, nothing of the kind. It is perhaps the best possible solution. I trust, Mr Holder, that you are nearing the end of your troubles.'

'Ha! You say so! You have heard something, Mr Holmes; you have learned something! Where are the gems?'

'You would not think £1000 apiece an excessive sum for them?'

'I would pay ten.'

'That would be unnecessary. Three thousand will cover the matter. And there is a little reward, I fancy. Have you your cheque-book? Here is a pen. Better make it out for £4000.'

With a dazed face the banker made out the required cheque. Holmes walked over to his desk, took out a little triangular piece of gold with three gems in it, and threw it down upon the table.

With a shriek of joy our client clutched it up.

'You have it!' he gasped. 'I am saved! I am saved!'

The reaction of joy was as passionate as his grief had been, and he hugged his recovered gems to his bosom.

'There is one other thing you owe, Mr Holder,' said Sherlock Holmes rather sternly.

'Owe!' He caught up a pen. 'Name the sum, and I will pay it.'

'No, the debt is not to me. You owe a very humble apology to that noble lad, your son, who has carried himself in this matter as I should be proud to see my own son do, should I ever chance to have one.'

'Then it was not Arthur who took them?'

'I told you yesterday, and I repeat to-day, that it was not.'

'You are sure of it! Then let us hurry to him at once to let him know that the truth is known.'

'He knows it already. When I had cleared it all up I had an interview with him, and finding that he would not tell me the story, I told it to him, on which he had to confess that I was right and to add the very few details which were not yet quite clear to me. Your news of this morning, however, may open his lips.'

'For heaven's sake, tell me, then, what is this extraordinary mystery!'

'I will do so, and I will show you the steps by which I reached it. And let me say to you, first, that which it is hardest for me to say and for you to hear: there has been an understanding between Sir George Burnwell and your niece Mary. They have now fled together.'

'My Mary? Impossible!'

'It is unfortunately more than possible; it is certain. Neither you nor your son knew the true character of this man when you admitted him into your family circle. He is one of the most dangerous men in England – a ruined gambler, an absolutely desperate villain, a man without heart or conscience. Your niece knew nothing of such men. When he breathed his vows to her, as he had done to a hundred before her, she flattered herself that she alone had touched his heart. The devil knows best what he said, but at least she became his tool and was in the habit of seeing him nearly every evening.'

'I cannot, and I will not, believe it!' cried the banker with an ashen face.

'I will tell you then, what occurred in your house last night. Your niece, when you had, as she thought, gone to your room, slipped down and talked to her lover through the window which leads into the stable lane. His footmarks had pressed right through the snow, so long had he stood there. She told him of the coronet. His wicked lust for gold kindled at the news, and he bent her to his will. I have no doubt that she loved you, but there are women in whom the love of a lover extinguishes all other loves, and I think that she must have been one. She had hardly listened to his instructions when she saw you coming downstairs, on which she closed the window rapidly and told you about one of the servants' escapade with her wooden-legged lover, which was all perfectly true.

'Your boy, Arthur, went to bed after his interview with you, but he slept badly on account of his uneasiness about his club debts. In the middle of the night he heard a soft tread pass his door, so he rose and, looking out, was surprised to see his cousin walking very stealthily along the passage until she disappeared into your dressing-room. Petrified with astonishment, the lad slipped on some clothes and waited there in the dark to see what would come of this strange affair. Presently she emerged from the room again, and in the light of the passage-lamp your son saw that she carried the precious coronet in her hands. She passed down the stairs, and he, thrilling with horror, ran along and slipped behind the curtain near your door, whence he could see what passed in the hall beneath. He saw her stealthily open the window, hand out the coronet to someone in the gloom, and then closing it once more hurry back to her room, passing quite close to where he stood hid behind the curtain.

'As long as she was on the scene he could not take any action without a horrible exposure of the woman whom he loved. But the instant that she was gone he realised how crushing a misfortune this would be for you, and how all-important it was to set it right. He rushed down, just as he was, in his bare feet, opened the window, sprang out into the snow, and ran down the lane, where he could see a dark figure in the moonlight. Sir George Burnwell tried to get away, but Arthur caught him, and there was a struggle between them, your lad tugging at one side of the coronet, and his opponent at the other. In the scuffle, your son struck Sir George and cut him over the eye. Then something suddenly snapped, and your son, finding that he had the coronet in his hands, rushed back, closed the window, ascended to your room, and had just observed that the coronet had been twisted in the struggle and was endeavouring to straighten it when you appeared upon the scene.'

'Is it possible?' gasped the banker.

'You then roused his anger by calling him names at a moment when he felt that he had deserved your warmest thanks. He could not explain the true state of affairs without betraying one who certainly deserved little enough consideration at his hands. He took the more chivalrous view, however, and preserved her secret.'

'And that was why she shrieked and fainted when she saw the coronet,' cried Mr Holder. 'Oh, my God! what a blind fool I have been! And his asking to be allowed to go out for five minutes! The dear fellow wanted to see if the missing piece were at the scene of the struggle. How cruelly I have misjudged him!'

'When I arrived at the house,' continued Holmes, 'I at once went very carefully round it to observe if there were any traces in the snow which might help me. I knew that none had fallen since the evening before, and also that there had been a strong frost to preserve impressions. I passed along the tradesmen's path, but found it all trampled down and indistinguishable. Just beyond it, however, at the far side of the kitchen door, a woman had stood and talked with a man, whose round impressions on one side showed that he had a wooden leg. I could even tell that they had been disturbed, for the woman had run back swiftly to the door, as was shown by the deep toe and light heel marks, while Wooden-leg had waited a little and then had gone away. I thought at the time that this might be the maid and her sweetheart, of whom you had already spoken to me, and inquiry showed it was so. I passed round the garden without seeing anything more than random tracks, which I took to be the police, but when I got into the stable lane a very long and complex story was written in the snow in front of me.

'There was a double line of tracks of a booted man, and a second double line which I saw with delight belonged to a man with naked feet. I was at once convinced from what you had told me that the latter was your son. The first had walked both ways, but the other had run swiftly, and as his tread was marked in places over the depression of the boot, it was obvious that he had passed after the other. I followed them up and found they led to the hall window, where Boots had worn all the snow away while waiting. Then I walked to the other end, which was a hundred yards or more down the lane. I saw where Boots had faced round, where the snow was cut up as though there had been a struggle, and finally, where a few drops of blood had fallen, to show me that I was not mistaken. Boots had then run down the lane, and another little smudge of blood showed that it was he who had been hurt. When he came to the highroad at the other end, I found that the pavement had been cleared, so there was an end to that clue.

'On entering the house, however, I examined, as you remember, the sill and framework of the hall window with my lens, and I could at once see that someone had passed out. I could distinguish the outline of an instep where the wet foot had been placed in coming in. I was then beginning to be able to form an opinion as to what had occurred. A man had waited outside the window; someone had brought the gems; the deed had been overseen by your son; he had pursued the thief; had struggled with him; they had each tugged at the coronet, their united strength causing injuries which neither alone could have effected. He had returned with the prize, but had left a fragment in the grasp of his opponent. So far I was clear. The question now was, who was the man and who was it brought him the coronet?

'It is an old **maxim** of mine that when you have excluded the impossible, whatever remains, however improbable, must be the truth. Now, I knew that it was not you who had brought it down, so there only remained your niece and the maids. But if it were the maids, why should your son allow himself to be accused in their place? There could be no possible reason. As he loved his cousin, however, there was an excellent explanation why he should retain her secret – the more so as the secret was a disgraceful one. When I remembered that you had seen her at the window, and how she had fainted on seeing the coronet again, my conjecture became a certainty.

'And who could it be who was her **confederate**? A lover evidently, for who else could outweigh the love and gratitude

maxim: rule
confederate: partner in crime

which she must feel to you? I knew that you went out little, and that your circle of friends was a very limited one. But among them was Sir George Burnwell. I had heard of him before as being a man of evil reputation among women. It must have been he who wore those boots and retained the missing gems. Even though he knew that Arthur had discovered him, he might still flatter himself that he was safe, for the lad could not say a word without compromising his own family.

'Well, your own good sense will suggest what measures I took next. I went in the shape of a loafer to Sir George's house, managed to pick up an acquaintance with his **valet**, learned that his master had cut his head the night before, and, finally, at the expense of six shillings, made all sure by buying a pair of his cast-off shoes. With these I journeyed down to Streatham and saw that they exactly fitted the tracks.'

'I saw an ill-dressed vagabond in the lane yesterday evening,' said Mr Holder.

'Precisely. It was I. I found that I had my man, so I came home and changed my clothes. It was a delicate part which I had to play then, for I saw that a prosecution must be avoided to avert scandal, and I knew that so astute a villain would see that our hands were tied in the matter. I went and saw him. At first, of course, he denied everything. But when I gave him every particular that had occurred, he tried to bluster and took down a **life-preserver** from the wall. I knew my man, however, and I clapped a pistol to his head before he could strike. Then he became a little more reasonable. I told him that we would give him a price for the stones he held – £1000 apiece. That brought out the first signs of grief that he had shown. "Why, dash it all!" said he, "I've let them go at six hundred for the three!" I soon managed to get the address of the receiver who had them, on promising him that there would be no prosecution. Off I set to him, and after much **chaffering** I got our stones at £1000 apiece. Then I looked in upon your son, told him that all was right, and eventually got

---

valet: manservant
life-preserver: heavy wooden stick
chaffering: bargaining

to my bed about two o'clock, after what I may call a really hard day's work.'

'A day which has saved England from a great public scandal,' said the banker, rising. 'Sir, I cannot find words to thank you, but you shall not find me ungrateful for what you have done. Your skill has indeed exceeded all that I have heard of it. And now I must fly to my dear boy to apologise to him for the wrong which I have done him. As to what you tell me of poor Mary, it goes to my very heart. Not even your skill can inform me where she is now.'

'I think that we may safely say,' returned Holmes, 'that she is wherever Sir George Burnwell is. It is equally certain, too, that whatever her sins are, they will soon receive a more than sufficient punishment.'

Non-fiction passages linked to
The Adventure of the Beryl Coronet
(1892)

Social scandal and 'dishonour' in the late nineteenth century

Queen Victoria's son, Edward Prince of Wales, was linked with a series of scandals in the 1880s and 1890s. They show just how fearful a respectable banker like Mr Holder would be of Arthur disgracing the family name, in an age when strict moral standards were expected:

The hint of scandal was never far from the Prince's companions. In 1885 Sir Charles Dilke, by now a close friend of the prince, was cited as co-respondent in the Crawford divorce case. In 1889 the Prince heard that Lord Arthur Somerset (Podge as he was known to his friends) had been discovered in a homosexual brothel during a police raid. This incident was hushed up to Prince Edward's satisfaction and the 'unfortunate lunatic' was allowed to flee the country. There was also a good deal of 'hushing-up' of the activities of Edward's own son, Albert Victor, whose debauchery became a serious worry to his parents.

Then in 1891 Edward found *himself* in a public court. During September 1890 he had stayed at Tranby Croft, the house of Arthur Wilson, for the St Leger race meeting. The evenings were given over to the popular, but illegal, game of baccarat. Wilson's son noticed one of the players, Sir William Gordon-Cumming, indulging in *la pousette* – a cheating device which enabled the player to vary the size of his stake after he had seen the cards held by himself and the bank. In two evenings Sir William had won £225 using this underhand manoeuvre. He had been observed by five witnesses.

Cumming sought the advice of Prince Edward but was told there was no use denying the charge. He agreed to sign a pledge never to play cards again, a pledge that bound all the signatories to silence. To this document Prince Edward put his name. Unfortunately, renewed rumours of Sir William's conduct broke out in 1891 and he felt obliged to bring his accusors to court in an attempt to clear his name.

The Prince did everything to hinder his efforts, but an appearance in court for the heir to the throne was inevitable. The case against the Prince was based on his encouragement of an illegal game and his disregard of Article 42 of Queen's Regulations, which laid down that dishonourable conduct by an officer, if witnessed by a fellow officer, must be reported to the offender's commanding officer.

The Prince attended court regularly from 1 to 9 June. During his own testimony he declared his confidence in those who had claimed to see Sir William cheating. After that the result was never really in doubt and the verdict was given in favour of the defendants. Gordon-Cumming was promptly expelled from the army, his clubs and society in general. His reputation, and therefore his life, was in ruins.

Keith Middlemass, 1972

Leisure among the upper classes around 1900

The kind of 'high society' life that Arthur was leading in London with Sir George Burnwell is shown, by this account, to be a typical evening out at the theatre. Notice the preoccupation with status and social reputation:

The social side of the thing is to be seen in visits paid from box to box in the intervals, and the smoking foyer is a centre where men meet to compare notes, though it is certain the note will not be concerned so much with the play as with the people who are present. 'Isn't Lady So-and-So looking remarkably well tonight? Wonder how she does it – She's fifty if she's a day! Wonderful! And look at little Laura! She's another wonder! Did you see *he* was in the box? Well, if her husband can stand it, it's all right, I suppose.' And so on and so on.

Somewhere around midnight the play comes to an end. Perhaps you go home, or perhaps you go to supper at somebody else's, for there are some superb supper-parties given after the play's over. Or you may go to one of the clubs, where you will have something to eat and exchange more gossip about your neighbours.

Robert Machray, 1902

CLUSTER 2

Strange and Supernatural

The Superstitious Man's Story
Thomas Hardy

'There was something very strange about William's death – very strange indeed!' sighed a melancholy man in the back of the van. It was the **seedsman's father**, who had hitherto kept silence.

'And what might that have been?' asked Mr Lackland.

'William, as you may know, was a curious, silent man; you could feel when he came near 'ee; and if he was in the house or anywhere behind your back without your seeing him, there seemed to be something clammy in the air, as if a cellar door was opened close by your elbow. Well, one Sunday, at a time that William was in very good health to all appearance, the bell that was ringing for church went very heavy all of a sudden; the **sexton**, who told me o't, said he'd not known the bell go so heavy in his hand in years – and he feared it meant a death in the parish. That was on the Sunday, as I say. During the week after, it chanced that William's wife was staying up late one night to finish her ironing, she doing the washing for Mr and Mrs Hardcome. Her husband had finished his supper and gone to bed as usual some hour or two before. While she ironed she heard him coming downstairs; he stopped to put on his boots at the stair-foot, where he always left them, and then came on into the living-room where she was ironing, passing through it towards the door, this being the only way from the staircase to the outside of the house. No word was said on either side, William not being a man given to much speaking, and his wife being occupied with her work. He went out and closed the door behind him. As her husband had now and then gone out in this way at night before when unwell, or unable to sleep for want of a pipe, she took no particular notice, and continued at

---

seedsman's father: the story's narrator (he is a passenger in a horse-drawn wagon taking some villagers home to Longpuddle)
sexton: church warden

her ironing. This she finished shortly after, and as he had not come in she waited a while for him, putting away the irons and things, and preparing the table for his breakfast in the morning. Still he did not return, and supposing him not far off, and wanting to get to bed herself, tired as she was, she left the door unbarred and went to the stairs, after writing on the back of the door with chalk: *Mind and do the door* (because he was a forgetful man).

'To her great surprise, and I might say alarm, on reaching the foot of the stairs his boots were standing there as they always stood when he had gone to rest; going up to their chamber she found him in bed sleeping as sound as a rock. How he could have got back again without her seeing or hearing him was beyond her comprehension. It could only have been by passing behind her very quietly while she was bumping with the iron. But this notion did not satisfy her: it was surely impossible that she should not have seen him come in through a room so small. She could not unravel the mystery, and felt very queer and uncomfortable about it. However, she would not disturb him to question him then, and went to bed herself.

'He rose and left for his work very early the next morning, before she was awake, and she waited his return to breakfast with much anxiety for an explanation, for thinking over the matter by daylight made it seem only the more startling. When he came in to the meal he said, before she could put her question, "What's the meaning of them words chalked on the door?"

'She told him, and asked him about his going out the night before. William declared that he had never left the bedroom after entering it, having in fact undressed, lain down, and fallen asleep directly, never once waking till the clock struck five, and he rose up to go to his labour.

'Betty Privett was as certain in her own mind that he did go out as she was of her own existence, and was little less certain that he did not return. She felt too disturbed to argue with him, and let the subject drop as though she must have been mistaken. When she was walking down Longpuddle Street later in the day she met Jim Weedle's daughter Nancy, and said, "Well, Nancy, you do look sleepy to-day!"

'"Yes, Mrs Privett," says Nancy. "Now don't tell anybody, but I don't mind letting you know what the reason o't is. Last night, being Old Midsummer Eve, some of us went to church porch, and didn't get home till near one."

'"Did ye?" says Mrs Privett. "Old Midsummer yesterday, was it? Faith I didn't think whe'r 'twas Midsummer or Michaelmas; I'd too much work to do."

'"Yes. And we were frightened enough, I can tell 'ee, by what we saw."

'"What did ye see?"

'(You may not remember, **sir**, having gone off to foreign parts so young, that on Midsummer Night it is believed hereabout that the faint shapes of all the folk in the parish who are going to be at death's door within the year can be seen entering the church. Those who get over their illness come out again after a while; those that are doomed to die do not return.)

'"What did you see?" asked William's wife.

'"Well," says Nancy, backwardly – "we needn't tell what we saw, or who we saw."

'"You saw my husband," says Betty Privett, in a quiet way.

'"Well, since you put it so," says Nancy, hanging fire, "we – thought we did see him; but it was darkish, and we was frightened, and of course it might not have been he."

'"Nancy, you needn't mind letting it out, though 'tis kept back in kindness. And he didn't come out of church again: I know it as well as you."

'Nancy did not answer yes or no to that, and no more was said. But three days after, William Privett was mowing with John Chiles in Mr Hardcome's meadow, and in the heat of the day they sat down to eat their bit o' lunch under a tree, and empty their flagon. Afterwards both of 'em fell asleep as they sat. John Chiles was the first to wake, and as he looked towards his fellow-mower he saw one of those great white **miller's-souls** as we call 'em – that is to say, a miller-moth – come from William's open mouth while he slept, and fly straight away. John thought

---

sir: a Longpuddle man who is returning from abroad
miller's-souls: large moths

it odd enough, as William had worked in a mill for several years when he was a boy. He then looked at the sun, and found by the place o't that they had slept a long while, and as William did not wake, John called him and said it was high time to begin work again. He took no notice, and then John went up and shook him, and found he was dead.

'Now on that very day old Philip Hookhorn was down at Longpuddle Spring dipping up a **pitcher** of water; and as he turned away, who should he see coming down to the spring on the other side but William, looking very pale and odd. This surprised Philip Hookhorn very much, for years before that time William's little son – his only child – had been drowned in that spring while at play there, and this had so preyed upon William's mind that he'd never been seen near the spring afterwards, and had been known to go half a mile out of his way to avoid the place. On inquiry, it was found that William in body could not have stood by the spring, being in the **mead** two miles off; and it also come out that the time at which he was seen at the spring was the very time when he died.'

---

pitcher: bucket
mead: meadow

Non-fiction passages linked to
The Superstitious Man's Story (1891)

Superstitions about death

Thomas Hardy came from Dorset. The omens of William's death were commonly believed by people in that part of the country. However, signs warning of a death are legendary all over Britain. Many of them are centuries old. Here is a selection:

Moths and butterflies. 'It be an ill sign to the dying if a dark winged moth make at the bed light and fall at it, but it be a good sign should a light winged one come thrice and go its way unharmed. Even if it do fail at it, it doth say nothing worse than the ailing one will soon die but that the death shall be the freeing of a happy soul' (1828). 'A large butterfly or moth seen in the room of a dying person is sometimes believed to be the soul quitting the body. It must not be killed' (1992).

Broken mirrors. 'It is about the unluckiest thing which can well befall a mortal this side the stars, to break a looking-glass, for it is a sure prognostic of family death. "Ad raather thad done owt nah as that!" we have known a woman say to her child, to whom this misfortune had happened, weeping the while, in sheer expectation of what was to come' (1861). 'Breaking a looking-glass betokens a mortality in the family, commonly the master' (1787).

Hair in the fire. 'If a person's hair, when thrown into the fire, blazes instantly, he or she will live long; but if it smudges away, or for any length of time, they will die soon' (1861). 'When a young woman combed her hair at night, she put every loose strand in the fire. If the hair did not burn, it meant that she would one day drown' (1970).

Dogs howling. 'Got a letter to say my Aunt Ellen was dead. I expected it quite, for a dog came in yesterday morning and howl'd piteously' (1863). 'Sweep added omen to superstition by sitting under the window and howling like a Banshee. For some days Sweep and I were absent, fishing. When I returned, I found on my mantelpiece a black-edged letter' (1873).

Clocks stopping. 'In my mother's home in Suffolk it was considered extremely unlucky if the old Dutch clock stopped. It was supposed to have done so when my grandfather and my maiden aunt died' (1953). 'The clock, which stopped before his mother and father died, stopped just before his son, aged nine, was burned to death in a haystack fire' (1961).

Three lighted candles. 'A few months since an Irish girl hastily blew out a candle placed near two others on her toilet table, saying "Three brings death"'(1906). 'Without thinking what she was doing, she lit three candles. Her husband hastily blew one of them out. 'Do thee know what 'ee have done? 'Tis three lighted candles that be put beside a coffin. 'Twill be cold death for we within a year"' (1930).

The Dictionary of Superstitions, 1993

The Trial for Murder
Charles Dickens

It does not **signify** how many years ago, or how few, a certain murder was committed in England, which attracted great attention. We hear more than enough of murderers as they rise in succession to their atrocious eminence, and I would bury the memory of this particular brute, if I could, as his body was buried, in Newgate Jail. I purposely abstain from giving any direct clue to the criminal's **individuality**.

When the murder was first discovered, no suspicion fell – or I ought rather to say, for I cannot be too precise in my facts, it was nowhere publicly hinted that any suspicion fell – on the man who was afterwards brought to trial. As no reference was at that time made to him in the newspapers, it is obviously impossible that any description of him can at that time have been given in the newspapers. It is essential that this fact be remembered.

Unfolding at breakfast my morning paper, containing the account of that first discovery, I found it to be deeply interesting, and I read it with close attention. I read it twice, if not three times. The discovery had been made in a bedroom, and, when I laid down the paper, I was aware of a flash – rush – flow – I do not know what to call it – no word I can find is satisfactorily descriptive – in which I seemed to see that bedroom passing through my room, like a picture impossibly painted on a running river. Though almost instantaneous in its passing, it was perfectly clear; so clear that I distinctly, and with a sense of relief, observed the absence of the dead body from the bed.

It was no romantic place that I had this curious sensation, but in **chambers** in Piccadilly, very near to the corner of St

signify: matter
individuality: identity
chambers: furnished rooms

James's Street. It was entirely new to me. I was in my easy-chair at the moment, and the sensation was accompanied with a peculiar shiver which started the chair from its position. (But it is to be noted that the chair ran easily on castors). I went to one of the windows (there are two in the room, and the room is on the second floor) to refresh my eyes with the moving objects down in Piccadilly. It was a bright autumn morning, and the street was sparkling and cheerful. The wind was high.

As I looked out, it brought down from the Park a quantity of fallen leaves, which a gust took, and whirled into a spiral pillar. As the pillar fell and the leaves dispersed, I saw two men on the opposite side of the way, going from West to East. They were one behind the other. The foremost man often looked back over his shoulder. The second man followed him, at a distance of some thirty paces, with his right hand menacingly raised. First, the **singularity** and steadiness of this threatening gesture in so public a thoroughfare attracted my attention; and next, the more remarkable circumstance that nobody heeded it. Both men threaded their way among the other passengers with a smoothness hardly consistent even with the action of walking on a pavement; and no single creature, that I could see, gave them place, touched them, or looked after them. In passing before my windows, they both stared up at me. I saw their faces very distinctly, and I knew that I could recognise them anywhere. Not that I consciously noticed anything very remarkable in either face, except that the man who went first had an unusually **lowering** appearance, and that the face of the man who followed him was of the colour of impure wax.

I am a bachelor, and my **valet** and his wife constitute my whole establishment. My occupation is in a certain Branch Bank, and I wish that my duties as head of a Department were as light as they are popularly supposed to be. They kept me in town that autumn, when I stood in need of change. I was not ill, but I was not well. My reader is to make the most that can be reasonably made of my feeling jaded, having a depressing

singularity: unusualness
lowering: scowling
valet: manservant

sense upon me of a monotonous life, and being 'slightly dyspeptic'. I am assured by my renowned doctor that my real state of health at that time justifies no stronger description, and I quote his own from his written answer to my request for it.

As the circumstances of the murder, gradually unravelling, took stronger and stronger possession of the public mind, I kept them away from mine by knowing as little about them as was possible in the midst of the universal excitement. But I knew that a verdict of Wilful Murder had been found against the suspected murderer, and that he had been committed to Newgate for trial. I also knew that his trial had been postponed over one Sessions of the Central Criminal Court, on the ground of general prejudice and want of time for the preparation of the defence. I may further have known, but I believe I did not, when, or about when, the Sessions to which his trial stood postponed would come on.

My sitting-room, bedroom, and dressing-room, are all on one floor. With the last there is no communication but through the bedroom. True, there is a door in it, once communicating with the staircase; but a part of the fitting of my bath has been – and had then been for some years – fixed across it. At the same period, and as a part of the same arrangement, the door had been nailed up and canvased over.

I was standing in my bedroom late one night, giving some directions to my servant before he went to bed. My face was towards the only available door of communication with the dressing-room, and it was closed. My servant's back was towards that door. While I was speaking to him I saw it open, and a man look in, who very earnestly and mysteriously beckoned to me. That man was the man who had gone second of the two along Piccadilly, and whose face was the colour of impure wax.

The figure, having beckoned, drew back, and closed the door. With no longer pause than was made by my crossing the bedroom, I opened the dressing-room door, and looked in. I had a lighted candle already in my hand. I felt no inward expectation of seeing the figure in the dressing-room, and I did not see it there.

Conscious that my servant stood amazed, I turned round to him, and said: 'Derrick, could you believe that in my cool senses I fancied I saw a . . .' As I there laid my hand upon his breast, with a sudden start he trembled violently, and said: 'O Lord, yes, Sir! A dead man beckoning!'

Now I do not believe that this John Derrick, my trusty and attached servant for more than twenty years, had any impression whatever of having seen any such figure, until I touched him. The change in him was so startling, when I touched him, that I fully believe he derived his impression in some **occult** manner from me at that instant.

I bade John Derrick bring some brandy, and I gave him a dram, and was glad to take one myself. Of what had preceded that night's phenomenon, I told him not a single word. Reflecting on it, I was absolutely certain that I had never seen that face before, except on the one occasion in Piccadilly. Comparing its expression when beckoning at the door with its expression when it had stared up at me as I stood at my window, I came to the conclusion that on the first occasion it had sought to fasten itself upon my memory, and that on the second it had made sure of being immediately remembered.

I was not very comfortable that night, though I felt a certainty, difficult to explain, that the figure would not return. At daylight I fell into a heavy sleep, from which I was awakened by John Derrick's coming to my bedside with a paper in his hand.

This paper, it appeared, had been the subject of an **altercation** at the door between its bearer and my servant. It was a summons to me to serve upon a Jury at the forthcoming Sessions of the Central Criminal Court at the Old Bailey. I had never before been summoned on such a Jury, as John Derrick well knew. He believed – I am not certain at this hour whether with reason or otherwise – that that class of Jurors were customarily chosen on a lower qualification than mine, and he had at first refused to accept the summons. The man who served it had taken the matter very coolly. He had said that my

occult: supernatural
altercation: argument

attendance or non-attendance was nothing to him; there the summons was; and I should deal with it at my own peril, and not at his.

For a day or two I was undecided whether to respond to this call, or take no notice of it. I was not conscious of the slightest mysterious bias, influence, or attraction, one way or other. Of that I am as strictly sure as of every other statement that I make here. Ultimately I decided, as a break in the monotony of my life, that I would go.

The appointed morning was a raw morning in the month of November. There was a dense brown fog in Piccadilly, and it become positively black and in the last degree oppressive East of Temple Bar. I found the passages and staircases of the Court-House flaringly lighted with gas, and the Court itself similarly illuminated. I *think* that, until I was conducted by officers into the Old Court and saw its crowded state, I did not know that the Murderer was to be tried that day. I *think* that, until I was so helped into the Old Court with considerable difficulty, I did not know into which of the two Courts sitting my summons would take me. But this must not be received as a **positive assertion**, for I am not completely satisfied in my mind on either point.

I took my seat in the place appropriated to Jurors in waiting, and I looked about the Court as well as I could through the cloud of fog and breath that was heavy in it. I noticed a black vapour hanging like a murky curtain outside the great windows, and I noticed the stifled sound of wheels on the straw or tan that was littered in the street; also, the hum of the people gathered there, which a shrill whistle, or a louder song or hail than the rest, occasionally pierced. Soon afterwards the Judges, two in number, entered, and took their seats. The buzz in the Court was awfully hushed. The direction was given to put the Murderer to the bar. He appeared there. And in that same instant I recognised in him the first of the two men who had gone down Piccadilly.

If my name had been called then, I doubt if I could have answered to it audibly. But it was called about sixth or eighth in

---

positive assertion: absolute fact

the panel, and I was by that time able to say 'Here!' Now, observe. As I stepped into the box, the prisoner, who had been looking on attentively, but with no sign of concern, became violently agitated, and beckoned to his attorney. The prisoner's wish to challenge me was so manifest, that it occasioned a pause, during which the attorney, with his hand upon the dock, whispered with his client, and shook his head. I afterward had it from that gentleman, that the prisoner's first affrighted words to him were: 'At all **hazards**, challenge that man!' But that, as he would give no reason for it, and admitted that he had not ever known my name until he heard it called and I appeared, it was not done.

Both on the ground already explained, that I wish to avoid reviving the unwholesome memory of that Murderer, and also because a detailed account of his long trial is by no means indispensable to my narrative, I shall confine myself to such incidents in the ten days and nights during which we, the Jury, were kept together, as directly bear on my own curious personal experience. It is in that, and not in the Murderer, that I seek to interest my reader. It is to that, and not to a page of the Newgate Calendar, that I beg attention.

I was chosen Foreman of the Jury. On the second morning of the trial, after evidence had been taken for two hours (I heard the church clocks strike), happening to cast my eyes over my brother jurymen, I found an inexplicable difficulty in counting them. I counted them several times, yet always with the same difficulty. In short, I made them one too many.

I touched the brother juryman whose place was next to me, and I whispered to him: 'Oblige me by counting us.' He looked surprised by the request, but turned his head and counted. 'Why,' says he, suddenly, 'we are thirt . . .; but no, it's not possible. No. We are twelve.'

According to my counting that day, we were always right in detail, but in **the gross** we were always one too many. There was no appearance – no figure – to account for it; but I had now an inward **foreshadowing** of the figure that was surely coming.

---

hazards: costs
the gross: total
foreshadowing: premonition

The Jury were housed at the London Tavern. We all slept in one large room on separate tables, and we were constantly in the charge and under the eye of the officer sworn to hold us in safe-keeping. I see no reason for suppressing the real name of that officer. He was intelligent, highly polite, and obliging, and (I was glad to hear) much respected in the City. He had an agreeable presence, good eyes, enviable black whiskers, and a fine sonorous voice. His name was Mr Harker.

When we turned into our twelve beds at night, Mr Harker's bed was drawn across the door. On the night of the second day, not being disposed to lie down, and seeing Mr Harker sitting on his bed, I went and sat beside him, and offered him a pinch of my snuff. As Mr Harker's hand touched mine in taking it from my box, a peculiar shiver crossed him, and he said: 'Who is this?'

Following Mr Harker's eyes, and looking along the room, I saw again the figure I expected – the second of the two men who had gone down Piccadilly. I rose, and advanced a few steps; then stopped, and looked round at Mr Harker. He was quite unconcerned, laughed, and said in a pleasant way: 'I thought for a moment we had a thirteenth juryman, without a bed. But I see it is the moonlight.'

Making no revelation to Mr Harker, but inviting him to take a walk with me to the end of the room, I watched what the figure did. It stood for a few moments by the bedside of each of my eleven brother jurymen, close to the pillow. It always went to the right-hand side of the bed, and always passed out crossing the foot of the next bed. It seemed, from the action of the head, merely to look down pensively at each recumbent figure. It took no notice of me, or of my bed, which was the nearest to Mr Harker's. It seemed to go out where the moonlight came in, through a high window, as by an aerial flight of stairs.

Next morning at breakfast, it appeared that everybody present had dreamed of the murdered man last night, except myself, and Mr Harker.

I now felt convinced that the second man who had gone down Piccadilly was the murdered man (so to speak), as if it had been borne into my comprehension by his immediate testimony. But even this took place, and in a manner for which I was not at all prepared.

On the fifth day of the trial, when the case for the prosecution was drawing to a close, a **miniature** of the murdered man, missing from his bedroom upon the discovery of the deed, and afterwards found in a hiding-place where the Murderer had been seen digging, was put in evidence. Having been identified by the witness under examination, it was handed up to the Bench, and thence handed down to be inspected by the Jury. As an officer in a black gown was making his way with it across to me, the figure of the second man who had gone down Piccadilly impetuously started from the crowd, caught the miniature from the officer, and gave it to me with his own hands, at the same time saying, in a low and hollow tone – before I saw the miniature, which was in a locket – '*I was younger then, and my face was not then drained of blood.*' It also came between me and the brother juryman to whom I would have given the miniature, and between him and the brother juryman to whom he would have given it, and so passed it on through the whole of our number, and back into my possession. Not one of them, however, detected this.

At table, and generally when we were shut up together in Mr Harker's custody, we had from the first naturally discussed the day's proceedings a good deal. On that fifth day, the case for the prosecution being closed, and we having that side of the question in a completed shape before us, our discussion was more animated and serious. Among our number was a **vestryman** – the densest idiot I have ever seen at large – who met the plainest evidence with the most preposterous objections, and who was sided with by two flabby **parochial parasites**; all the three impanelled from a district so delivered over to Fever that they ought to have been upon their own trial for five hundred Murders. When these mischievous blockheads were at their loudest, which was towards midnight, while some of us were

miniature: small portrait
vestry-man: vicar
parochial parasites: fawning friends of the vicar

already preparing for bed, I again saw the murdered man. He stood grimly behind them, beckoning to me. On my going towards them, and striking into the conversation, he immediately retired. This was the beginning of a separate series of appearances, confined to that long room in which *we* were confined. Whenever a knot of my brother jurymen laid their heads together, I saw the head of the murdered man among them. Whenever their comparison of notes was going against him, he would solemnly and irresistibly beckon to me.

It will be borne in mind that down to the production of the miniature, on the fifth day of the trial, I had never seen the Appearance in Court. Three changes occurred now that we entered on the case for the defence. Two of them I will mention together, first. The figure was now in Court continually, and it never there addressed itself to me, but always to the person who was speaking at the time. For instance: the throat of the murdered man had been cut straight across. In the opening speech for the defence, it was suggested that the deceased might have cut his own throat. At that very moment, the figure, with its throat in the dreadful condition referred to (this it had concealed before), stood at the speaker's elbow, motioning across and across its windpipe, now with the right hand, now with the left, vigorously suggesting to the speaker himself the impossibility of such a wound having been self-inflicted by either hand. For another instance: a witness to character, a woman, deposed to the prisoner's being the most amiable of mankind. The figure at that instant stood on the floor before her, looking her full in the face, and pointing out the prisoner's evil countenance with an extended arm and an outstretched finger.

The third change now to be added impressed me strongly as the most marked and striking of all. I do not theorise upon it; I accurately state it, and there leave it. Although the Appearance was not itself perceived by those whom it addressed, its coming close to such persons was invariably attended by some **trepidation of disturbance** on their part. It seemed to me as if it were prevented, by laws to which I was not amenable, from

---

trepidation of disturbance: sign of alarm

fully revealing itself to others, and yet as if it could visibly, dumbly, and darkly overshadow their minds. When the leading counsel for the defence suggested that hypothesis of suicide, and the figure stood at the learned gentleman's elbow, frightfully sawing at its severed throat, it is undeniable that the counsel faltered in his speech, lost for a few seconds the thread of his ingenious discourse, wiped his forehead with his handkerchief, and turned extremely pale. When the witness to character was confronted by the Appearance, her eyes most certainly did follow the direction of its pointed finger, and rest in great hesitation and trouble upon the prisoner's face. Two additional illustrations will suffice. On the eighth day of the trial, after a pause which was every day made early in the afternoon for a few minutes' rest and refreshment, I came back into court with the rest of the Jury some little time before the return of the Judges. Standing up in the box and looking about me, I thought the figure was not there, until, chancing to raise my eyes to the gallery, I saw it bending forward, and leaning over a very decent woman, as if to assure itself whether the Judges had resumed their seats or not. Immediately afterwards that woman screamed, fainted, and was carried out. So with the **venerable**, **sagacious**, and patient Judge who conducted the trial. When the case was over, and he settled himself and his papers to sum up, the murdered man, entering the Judge's door, advanced to his Lordship's desk, and looked eagerly over his shoulder at the pages of his notes which he was turning. A change came over his Lordship's face; his hand stopped; the peculiar shiver, that I knew so well, passed over him; he faltered: 'Excuse me, gentlemen, for a few moments. I am somewhat oppressed by the **vitiated** air,' and did not recover until he had drunk a glass of water.

Through all the monotony of six of those interminable ten days – the same Judges and others on the bench, the same Murderer in the dock, the same lawyers at the table, the same tones of question and answer rising to the roof of the Court,

venerable, sagacious: respected, wise
vitiated: tainted

the same scratching of the Judge's pen, the same ushers going in and out, the same lights kindled at the same hour when there had been any natural light of day, the same foggy curtain outside the great windows when it was foggy, the same rain pattering and dripping when it was rainy, the same footmarks of **turnkeys** and prisoner day after day on the same sawdust, the same keys locking and unlocking the same heavy doors – through all the wearisome monotony which made me feel as if I had been Foreman of the Jury for a vast period of time, and Piccadilly had flourished **coevally with Babylon**, the murdered man never lost one trace of his distinctness in my eyes, nor was he at any moment less distinct than anybody else. I must not omit, as a matter of fact, that I never once saw the Appearance which I call by the name of the murdered man look at the Murderer. Again and again I wondered 'why does he not?' But he never did.

Nor did he look at me, after the production of the miniature, until the last closing minutes of the trial arrived. We retired to consider, at seven minutes before ten at night. The idiotic vestry-man and his two parochial parasites gave us so much trouble that we twice returned into Court to beg to have certain extracts from the Judge's notes re-read. Nine of us had not the smallest doubt about these passages, neither, I believe, had any one in Court; the **dunder-headed triumvirate**, however, having no idea but obstruction, disputed them for that very reason. At length we prevailed, and finally the Jury returned into Court at ten minutes past twelve.

The murdered man at that time stood directly opposite the Jury box, on the other side of the Court. As I took my place, his eyes rested on me with great attention; he seemed satisfied, and slowly shook a great grey veil, which he carried on his arm for the first time, over his head and whole form. As I gave in our verdict, 'Guilty', the veil collapsed, all was gone, and his place was empty.

---

turnkeys: jailers
coevally with Babylon: at the same time as Babylon, an ancient city renowned for sin and wickedness
dunder-headed triumvirate: stupid trio

The murderer, being asked by the Judge, according to **usage**, whether he had anything to say before sentence of Death should be passed upon him, indistinctly muttered something which was described in the leading newspapers of the following day as 'a few rambling, incoherent, and half-audible words, in which he was understood to complain that he had not had a fair trial, because the Foreman of the Jury was **prepossessed** against him.' The remarkable declaration that he really made was this: *'My Lord, I knew I was a doomed man, when the Foreman of my Jury came into the box. My Lord, I knew he would never let me off, because, before I was taken, he somehow got to my bedside in the night, woke me, and put a rope round my neck.'*

usage: custom of a court hearing
prepossessed: prejudiced

Non-fiction passages linked to *The Trial for Murder* (1865)

Newgate Prison in the early nineteenth century

Before his trial, the accused man would have been held in Newgate Prison. Conditions there were appalling:

> The courtyard into which I was admitted [was] peopled with beings scarcely human, blaspheming, fighting, tearing each others' hair or gaming with a filthy pack of cards for the very clothes they wore … Nearly three hundred women, sent there for every gradation of crime, some tried, and some under sentence of death, were crowded together in the two wards and two cells … they slept on the floor, at times one hundred and twenty in one ward, without so much as a mat for bedding; and many of them were nearly naked.

Thomas Buxton, 1818

Dickens and the supernatural

Dickens was fascinated by the supernatural. Throughout his life, he had many ghostly experiences. This one may have been in his mind when he described the banker's blood turning cold as he 'saw', in a trance, the scene of the murder:

I suddenly (the temperature being then most violent) found an icy coldness come upon me, accompanied with a general stagnation of the blood, a numbness of the extremities, great bewilderment of mind, and a vague sense of wonder. I was walking at the time, and, on looking about me, found that I was in the frigid shadow of the Burlington Hotel. Then I recollected to have experienced the same sensations once precisely in that spot. A curious case, don't you think?

Charles Dickens, 1854

A public execution at Newgate

The accused man, having been found guilty, would have been hanged at Newgate. In the mid-nineteenth century, such hangings were a public spectacle, as the text on page 120 explains.

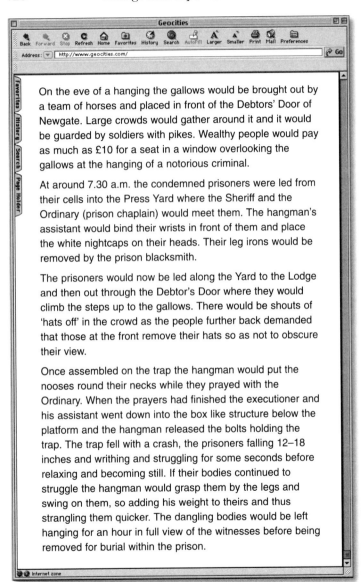

On the eve of a hanging the gallows would be brought out by a team of horses and placed in front of the Debtors' Door of Newgate. Large crowds would gather around it and it would be guarded by soldiers with pikes. Wealthy people would pay as much as £10 for a seat in a window overlooking the gallows at the hanging of a notorious criminal.

At around 7.30 a.m. the condemned prisoners were led from their cells into the Press Yard where the Sheriff and the Ordinary (prison chaplain) would meet them. The hangman's assistant would bind their wrists in front of them and place the white nightcaps on their heads. Their leg irons would be removed by the prison blacksmith.

The prisoners would now be led along the Yard to the Lodge and then out through the Debtor's Door where they would climb the steps up to the gallows. There would be shouts of 'hats off' in the crowd as the people further back demanded that those at the front remove their hats so as not to obscure their view.

Once assembled on the trap the hangman would put the nooses round their necks while they prayed with the Ordinary. When the prayers had finished the executioner and his assistant went down into the box like structure below the platform and the hangman released the bolts holding the trap. The trap fell with a crash, the prisoners falling 12–18 inches and writhing and struggling for some seconds before relaxing and becoming still. If their bodies continued to struggle the hangman would grasp them by the legs and swing on them, so adding his weight to theirs and thus strangling them quicker. The dangling bodies would be left hanging for an hour in full view of the witnesses before being removed for burial within the prison.

The Ostler
Wilkie Collins

I find an old man, fast asleep, in one of the stalls of the stable. It is midday, and rather a strange time for an **ostler** to devote to sleep. Something curious, too, about the man's face. A withered woebegone face. The eyebrows painfully contracted; the mouth fast set, and drawn down at the corners; the hollow cheeks sadly, and, as I cannot help fancying, prematurely wrinkled; the scanty, grizzled hair, telling weakly its own tale of some past sorrow or suffering. How fast he draws his breath, too, for a man asleep! He is talking in his sleep.

'Wake up!' I hear him say, in a quick whisper through his fast-clenched teeth. 'Wake up there! Murder! O Lord help me! Lord help me, alone in this place!'

He stops, and sighs again – moves one lean arm slowly, till it rests over his throat – shudders a little, and turns on his straw – the arm leaves his throat – the hand stretches itself out, and clutches at the side towards which he has turned, as if he fancies himself to be grasping at the edge of something. Is he waking! No – there is the whisper again; he is still talking in his sleep.

'Light grey eyes,' he says now, 'and a droop in the left eyelid. Yes! yes! – flaxen hair with a gold-yellow streak in it – all right, mother – fair, white arms with a down on them – little lady's hand, with a reddish look under the fingernails – and the knife – always the cursed knife – first on one side, then on the other. Aha! you she-devil, where's the knife? Never mind, mother – too late now. I've promised to marry, and marry I must. Murder! wake up there! for God's sake, wake up!'

At the last words his voice rises, and he grows so restless on a sudden, that I draw back quietly to the door. I see him shudder on the straw – his withered face grows distorted – he

---

ostler: stable-man

throws up both his hands with a quick, hysterical gasp; they strike against the bottom of the manger under which he lies; the blow awakens him; I have just time to slip through the door, before his eyes are fairly open and his senses are his own again.

What I have seen and heard has so startled and shocked me, that I feel my heart beating fast, as I softly and quickly retrace my steps across the inn-yard. The discomposure that is going on within me, apparently shows itself in my face; for, as I get back to the covered way leading to the inn stairs, the landlord, who is just coming out of the house to ring some bell in the yard, stops astonished, and asks what is the matter with me. I tell him what I have just seen.

'Aha!' says the landlord, with an air of relief. 'I understand now. Poor old chap! He was only dreaming his old dream over again. There's the queerest story – of a dreadful kind, too, mind you – connected with him and his dream, that ever was told.'

I entreat the landlord to tell me the story. After a little hesitation, he complies with my request.

Some years ago, there lived in the suburbs of a large sea-port town, on the west coast of England, a man in humble circumstances, by the name of Isaac Scatchard. His means of subsistence were derived from any employment that he could get, as an ostler; and, occasionally, when times went well with him, from temporary engagements in service, as stable-helper in private houses. Though a faithful, steady, and honest man, he got on badly in his calling. His ill-luck was **proverbial** among his neighbours. He was always missing good opportunities, by no fault of his own; and always living longest in service with amiable people who were not punctual payers of wages. 'Unlucky Isaac' was his nickname in his own neighbourhood – and no one could say that he did not richly deserve it.

With far more than one man's fair share of adversity to endure, Isaac had but one consolation to support him – and that was of the dreariest and most negative kind. He had no wife and children to increase his anxieties and add to the

---

proverbial: well-known

bitterness of his various failures in life. It might have been from mere **insensibility**, or it might have been from generous unwillingness to involve another in his own unlucky destiny – but the fact undoubtedly was, that he arrived at the middle term of life without marrying; and, what is much more remarkable, without once exposing himself, from eighteen to eight and thirty, to the **genial imputation** of ever having had a sweetheart. When he was out of service, he lived alone with his widowed mother. Mrs Scatchard was a woman above the average in her lowly station, as to capacities and manners. She had seen better days, as the phrase is; but she never referred to them in the presence of curious visitors; and, though perfectly polite to everyone who approached her, never cultivated any intimacies among her neighbours. She contrived to provide, hardly enough, for her simple wants, by doing rough work for the tailors; and always managed to keep a decent home for her son to return to whenever his ill-luck drove him out helpless into the world.

One bleak autumn, when Isaac was getting on fast towards forty, and when he was, as usual, out of place, through no fault of his own, he set forth from his mother's cottage on a long walk inland to a gentleman's seat, where he had heard that a stable-helper was required. It **wanted** then but two days of his birthday; and Mrs Scatchard, with her usual fondness, made him promise, before he started, that he would be back in time to keep that anniversary with her, in as festive a way as their poor means would allow. It was easy for him to comply with this request, even supposing he slept a night each way on the road. He was to start from home on Monday morning; and, whether he got the new place or not, he was to be back for his birthday dinner on Wednesday at two o'clock.

Arriving at his destination too late on the Monday night to make application for the stable-helper's place, he slept at the village inn, and in good time on the Tuesday morning, presented himself at the gentleman's house, to fill the vacant

insensibility: lack of feeling
genial imputation: pleasant rumour
wanted: fell short

situation. Here, again, his ill-luck pursued him an **inexorably** as ever. The excellent written testimonials, as to character, which he was able to produce, availed him nothing; his long walk had been taken in vain – only the day before, the stable-helper's place had been given to another man.

Isaac accepted this new disappointment resignedly, and as a matter of course. Naturally **slow in capacity**, he had the bluntness of sensibility and **phlegmatic** patience of disposition which frequently distinguish men with sluggishly-working mental powers. He thanked the gentleman's steward, with his usual quiet civility, for granting him an interview, and took his departure with no appearance of unusual depression in his face or manner. Before starting on his homeward walk, he made some inquiries at the inn, and ascertained that he might save a few miles, on his return, by following a new road. Furnished with full instructions, several times repeated, as to the various turnings he was to take, he set forth for his homeward journey, and walked on all day with only one stoppage for bread and cheese. Just as it was getting towards dark, the rain came on and the wind began to rise; and he found himself, to make matters worse, in a part of the country with which he was entirely unacquainted, though he knew himself to be some fifteen miles from home. The first house he found to inquire at was a lonely roadside inn, standing on the outskirts of a thick wood. Solitary as the place looked, it was welcome to a lost man who was also hungry, thirsty, footsore, and wet. The landlord was a civil, respectable-looking man; and the price he asked for a bed was reasonable enough. Isaac, therefore, decided on stopping comfortably at the inn for that night.

He was **constitutionally** a temperate man. His supper simply consisted of two rashers of bacon, a slice of home-made bread, and a pint of ale. He did not go to bed immediately after this moderate meal, but sat up with the landlord talking about his bad prospects and his long run of ill-luck, and diverging from

---

inexorably: persistently
slow in capacity: below average intelligence
phlegmatic: unemotional
constitutionally: by nature

these topics to the subject of horse-flesh and racing. Nothing was said either by himself, his host, or the few labourers who strayed into the taproom, which could, in the slightest degree, excite the very small and very dull imaginative faculty which Isaac Scatchard possessed.

At a little after eleven the house was closed. Isaac went round with the landlord and held the candle while the doors and lower-windows were being secured. He noticed with surprise the strength of the bolts, bars, and iron-sheathed shutters.

'You see, we are rather lonely here,' said the landlord. 'We never have had any attempts made to break in yet, but it's always as well to be on the safe side. When nobody is sleeping here, I am the only man in the house. My wife and daughter are timid, and the servant-girl takes after her missusses. Another glass of ale before you turn in? – No! – Well, how such a sober man as you comes to be out of place is more than I can make out, for one. – Here's where you're to sleep. You're our only lodger tonight, and I think you'll say my missus has done her best to make you comfortable. You're quite sure you won't have another glass of ale? – Very well. Good-night.'

It was half-past eleven by the clock in the passage as they went upstairs to the bedroom, the window of which looked on to the wood at the back of the house. Isaac locked the door, set his candle on the chest of drawers, and wearily got ready for bed. The bleak autumn wind was still blowing, and the solemn, monotonous, surging moan of it in the wood was dreary and awful to hear through the night-silence. Isaac felt strangely wakeful, and resolved, as he lay down in bed, to keep the candle alight until he began to grow sleepy; for there was something unendurably depressing in the bare idea of lying awake in the darkness, listening to the dismal, ceaseless moaning of the wind in the wood.

Sleep stole on him before he was aware of it. His eyes closed, and he fell off insensibly to rest, without having so much as thought of extinguishing the candle.

The first sensation of which he was conscious after sinking into slumber, was a strange shivering that ran through him suddenly from head to foot, and a dreadful sinking pain at the heart, such as he had never felt before. The shivering only disturbed his slumbers – the pain woke him instantly. In one moment he passed from a state of sleep to a state of wakefulness – his eyes wide open – his mental perceptions cleared on a sudden as if by a miracle.

The candle had burnt down nearly to the last morsel of tallow; but the top of the unsnuffed wick had just fallen off, and the light in the little room was, for the moment, fair and full. Between the foot of his bed and the closed door there stood a woman with a knife in her hand, looking at him. He was stricken speechless with terror, but he did not lose the **preternatural** clearness of his faculties; and he never took his eyes off the woman. She said not one word as they stared each other in the face; but she began to move slowly towards the left-hand side of the bed.

His eyes followed her. She was a fair, fine woman, with yellowish flaxen hair, and light grey eyes, with a droop in the left eyelid. He noticed those things and fixed them on his mind, before she was round at the side of the bed. Speechless, with no expression in her face, with no noise following her footfall – she came closer and closer – stopped – and slowly raised the knife. He laid his right arm over his throat to save it; but, as he saw the knife coming down, threw his hand across the bed to the right side, and jerked his body over that way, just as the knife descended on the mattress within an inch of his shoulder.

His eyes fixed on her arm and hand, as she slowly drew the knife out of the bed. A white, well-shaped arm, with a pretty down lying lightly over the fair skin. A delicate, lady's hand, with the crowning beauty of a pink flush under and round the fingernails.

She drew the knife out, and passed back again slowly to the foot of the bed; stopped there for a moment looking at him; then came on – still speechless, still with no expression on the blank, beautiful face, still with no sound following the stealthy footfalls – came on to the right side of the bed where he now lay. As she approached, she raised the knife again, and he drew

---

preternatural: exceptional

himself away to the left side. She struck, as before, right into the mattress, with a deliberate, perpendicularly-downward action of the arm. This time his eyes wandered from her to the knife. It was like the large clasp knives which he had often seen labouring men use to cut their bread and bacon with. Her delicate little fingers did not conceal more than two thirds of the handle; he noticed that it was made of buck-horn, clean and shining as the blade was, and looking like new.

For the second time she drew the knife out, concealed it in the wide sleeve of her gown, then stopped by the bedside, watching him. For an instant he saw her standing in that position – then the wick of the spent candle fell over into the socket. The flame diminished to a little blue point, and the room grew dark. A moment, or less, if possible, passed so – and then the wick flamed up, smokily, for the last time. His eyes were still looking eagerly over the right-hand side of the bed when the final flash of light came, but they discerned nothing. The fair woman with the knife was gone.

The conviction that he was alone again, weakened the hold of the terror that had struck him dumb up to this time. The preternatural sharpness which the very intensity of his panic had mysteriously imparted to his faculties, left them suddenly. His brain grew confused – his heart beat wildly – his ears opened for the first time since the appearance of the woman, to a sense of the woeful, ceaseless moaning of the wind among the trees. With the dreadful conviction of the reality of what he had seen, still strong within him, he leapt out of bed, and screaming – 'Murder! – Wake up, there, wake up!' – dashed headlong through the darkness to the door.

It was fast locked, exactly as he had left it on going to bed.

His cries on starting up, had alarmed the house. He heard the terrified, confused exclamations of women; he saw the master of the house approaching along the passage, with his burning rush-candle in one hand and his gun in the other.

'What is it?' asked the landlord, breathlessly.

Isaac could only answer in a whisper. 'A woman with a knife in her hand,' he gasped out. 'In my room – a fair, yellow-haired woman; she jobbed at me with the knife, twice over.'

The landlord's pale cheeks grew paler. He looked at Isaac eagerly by the flickering light of his candle; and his face began to get red again – his voice altered, too, as well as his complexion.

'She seems to have missed you twice,' he said.

'I dodged the knife as it came down,' Isaac went on, in the same scared whisper. 'It struck the bed each time.'

The landlord took his candle into the bedroom immediately. In less than a minute he came out again into the passage in a violent passion.

'The devil fly away with you and your woman with the knife! What do you mean by coming into a man's place and frightening his family out of their wits about a dream?'

'I'll leave your house,' said Isaac, faintly. 'Better out on the road, in rain and dark, on my way home, than back again in that room after what I've seen in it. Lend me a light to get on my clothes by, and tell me what I'm to pay.'

'Pay!' cried the landlord, leading the way with his light sulkily into the bedroom. 'You'll find your **score** on the slate when you go downstairs. I wouldn't have taken you in for all the money you've got about you, if I'd known your dreaming, screeching ways beforehand. Look at the bed. Where's the cut of a knife in it? Look at the window – is the lock bursted? Look at the door (which I heard you fasten myself) – is it broke in? A murdering woman with a knife in my house! You ought to be ashamed of yourself!'

Isaac answered not a word. He huddled on his clothes; and then they went downstairs together.

'Nigh on twenty minutes past two!' said the landlord, as they passed the clock. 'A nice time in the morning to frighten honest people out of their wits!'

Isaac paid his bill, and the landlord let him out at the front door, asking, with a grin of contempt, as he undid the strong fastenings, whether 'the murdering woman got in that way'. The rain had ceased; but the night was dark, and the wind bleaker than ever. Little did the darkness, or the cold, or the

---

score: bill

uncertainty about his way home, matter to Isaac. If he had been turned out into a wilderness in a thunderstorm, it would have been a relief, after what he had suffered in the bedroom of the inn.

What was the fair woman with the knife? The creature of a dream, or that other creature from the unknown world called among men by the name of ghost? He could make nothing of the mystery – had made nothing of it, even when it was midday on Wednesday, and when he stood, at last, after many times missing his road, once more on the doorstep of home.

His mother came out eagerly to receive him. His face told her in a moment that something was wrong.

'I've **lost the place**; but that's my luck. I dreamed an ill dream last night, mother – or, may be, I saw a ghost. Take it either way, it scared me out of my senses, and I'm not my own man again yet.'

'Isaac! your face frightens me. Come in to the fire. Come in, and tell mother all about it.'

He was as anxious to tell as she was to hear; for it had been his hope, all the way home, that his mother, with her quicker capacity and superior knowledge, might be able to throw some light on the mystery which he could not clear up for himself. His memory of the dream was still mechanically vivid, though his thoughts were entirely confused by it.

His mother's face grew paler and paler as he went on. She never interrupted him by so much as a single word; but when he had done, she moved her chair close to his, put her arm round his neck, and said to him:

'Isaac, you dreamed your ill dream on this Wednesday morning. What time was it when you saw the fair woman with the knife in her hand?'

Isaac reflected on what the landlord had said when they passed by the clock on his leaving the inn – allowed as nearly as he could for the time that must have elapsed between the unlocking of his bedroom door and the paying of his bill just before going away, and answered:

---

lost the place: did not get the job

'Somewhere about two o'clock in the morning.'

His mother suddenly quitted her hold of his neck, and struck her hands together with a gesture of despair.

'This Wednesday is your birthday Isaac; and two o'clock in the morning was the time when you were born!'

Isaac's capacities were not quick enough to catch the infection of his mother's superstitious dread. He was amazed and a little startled also, when she suddenly rose from her chair, opened her old writing-desk, took out pen and ink and paper, and then said to him:

'Your memory is but a poor one, Isaac, and now I'm an old woman, mine's not much better. I want all about this dream of yours to be as well known to both of us, years hence, as it is now. Tell me over again all you told me a minute ago, when you spoke of what the woman with the knife looked like.'

Isaac obeyed, and marvelled much as he saw his mother carefully set down on paper the very words that he was saying. 'Light grey eyes,' she wrote, as they came to the descriptive part, 'with a droop in the left eyelid. Flaxen hair, with a gold-yellow streak in it. White arms, with a down on them. Little lady's hand, with a reddish look about the fingernails. Clasp knife with a buck-horn handle, that seemed as good as new.' To these particulars, Mrs Scatchard added the year, month, day of the week, and time in the morning, when the woman of the dream appeared to her son. She then locked up the paper carefully in her writing-desk.

Neither on that day, nor on any day after, could her son **induce** her to return to the matter of the dream. She obstinately kept her thoughts about it to herself, and even refused to refer again to the paper in her writing-desk. Ere long, Isaac grew weary of attempting to make her break her resolute silence; and time, which sooner or later, wears out all things, gradually wore out the impression produced on him by the dream. He began by thinking of it carelessly, and he ended by not thinking of it at all. This result was the more easily brought about by the **advent** of some important changes for the better

induce: persuade
advent: arrival

in his prospects, which commenced not long after his terrible night's experience at the inn. He reaped at last the reward of his long and patient suffering under adversity, by getting an excellent place, keeping it for seven years, and leaving it, on the death of his master, not only with an excellent character, but also with a comfortable **annuity** bequeathed to him as a reward for saving his mistress's life in a carriage accident. Thus it happened that Isaac Scatchard returned to his old mother, seven years after the time of the dream at the inn, with an annual sum of money at his disposal, sufficient to keep them both in ease and independence for the rest of their lives.

The mother, whose health had been bad of late years, profited so much by the care bestowed on her and by freedom from money anxieties, that when Isaac's next birthday came round, she was able to sit up comfortably at table and dine with him.

On that day, as the evening drew on, Mrs Scatchard discovered that a bottle of tonic medicine – which she was accustomed to take, and in which she had fancied that a dose or more was still left – happened to be empty. Isaac immediately volunteered to go to the chemist's, and get it filled again. It was as rainy and bleak an autumn night as on the memorable past occasion when he lost his way and slept at the roadside inn.

On going to the chemist's shop, he was passed hurriedly by a poorly-dressed woman coming out of it. The glimpse he had of her face struck him, and he looked back after her as she descended the door-steps.

'You're noticing the woman?' said the chemist's apprentice behind the counter. 'It's my opinion there's something wrong with her. She's been asking for **laudanum** to put to a bad tooth. Master's out for half an hour; and I told her I wasn't allowed to sell poison to strangers in his absence. She laughed in a queer way, and said she would come back in half an hour. If she expects master to serve her, I think she'll be disappointed. It's a case of suicide, sir, if ever there was one yet.'

annuity: financial allowance
laudanum: liquid opium

These words added immeasurably to the sudden interest in the woman which Isaac had felt at the first sight of her face. After he had got the medicine-bottle filled, he looked about anxiously for her, as soon as he went out in the street. She was walking slowly up and down on the opposite side of the road. With his heart, very much to his own surprise, beating fast, Isaac crossed over and spoke to her.

He asked if she was in any distress. She pointed to her torn shawl, her scanty dress, her crushed, dirty bonnet – then moved under a lamp so as to let the light fall on her stern, pale, but still most beautiful face.

'I look like a comfortable, happy woman – don't I?' she said with a bitter laugh.

She spoke with a purity of intonation which Isaac had never heard before from other than ladies' lips. Her slightest actions seemed to have the easy negligent grace of a **thoroughbred** woman. Her skin, for all its poverty-stricken paleness, was as delicate as if her life had been passed in the enjoyment of every social comfort that wealth can purchase. Even her small, finely-shaped hands, gloveless as they were, had not lost their whiteness.

Little by little, in answer to his question, the sad story of the woman came out. There is no need to relate it here; it is told over and over again in Police Reports and paragraphs about Attempted Suicides.

'My name is Rebecca Murdoch,' said the woman, as she ended. 'I have ninepence left, and I thought of spending it at the chemist's over the way in securing a passage to the other world. Whatever it is, it can't be worse to me than this – so why should I stop here!'

Besides the natural compassion and sadness moved in his heart by what he heard, Isaac felt within him some mysterious influence at work all the time the woman was speaking, which utterly confused his ideas and almost deprived him of his powers of speech. All that he could say in answer to her last reckless words was, that he would prevent her from attempting

---

thoroughbred: aristocratic

her own life, if he followed her about all night to do it. His rough, trembling earnestness seemed to impress her.

'I won't occasion you that trouble,' she answered, when he repeated his threat. 'You have given me a fancy for living by speaking kindly to me. No need for the mockery of protestations and promises. You may believe me without them. Come to Fuller's Meadow tomorrow at twelve, and you will find me alive, to answer to myself. No! – no money. My ninepence will do to get me as good a night's lodging as I want.'

She nodded and left him. He made no attempt to follow – he felt no suspicion that she was deceiving him.

'It's strange, but I can't help believing her,' he said to himself – and walked away, bewildered, towards home.

On entering the house his mind was still so completely absorbed by its new subject of interest, that he took no notice of what his mother was doing when he came in with the bottle of medicine. She had opened her old writing-desk in his absence, and was now reading a paper attentively that lay inside it. On every birthday of Isaac's since she had written down the particulars of his dream from his own lips, she had been accustomed to read that same paper, and ponder over it in private.

The next day he went to Fuller's Meadow. He had done only right in believing her so **implicitly** – she was there, punctual to a minute, to answer for herself. The last-left faint defences in Isaac's heart against the fascination which a word or look from her began **inscrutably** to exercise over him, sank down and vanished before her for ever on that memorable morning.

When a man, previously insensible to the influence of women, forms an attachment in middle life, the instances are rare indeed, let the warning circumstances be what they may, in which he is found capable of freeing himself from the tyranny of the new ruling passion. The charm of being spoken to familiarly, fondly, and gratefully by a woman whose language and manners still retained enough of their early refinement to hint at the high social station that she had lost, would have

implicitly: completely
inscrutably: without reason

been dangerous luxury to a man of Isaac's rank at the age of twenty. But it was far more than that – it was certain ruin to him – now that his heart was opening unworthily to a new influence, at that middle time of life when strong feelings of all kinds, once implanted, strike root stubbornly in a man's moral nature. A few more stolen interviews after that first morning in Fuller's Meadow completed his **infatuation**. In less than a month from the time when he first met her, Isaac Scatchard had consented to give Rebecca Murdoch a new interest in existence, and a chance of recovering the character she had lost, by promising to make her his wife.

She had taken possession, not of his passions only, but of his **faculties** as well. All arrangements for the present and all plans for the future were of her devising. All the mind he had he put into her keeping. She directed him on every point; even instructing him how to break the news of his approaching marriage in the safest manner to his mother.

'If you tell her how you met me and who I am at first,' said the cunning woman, 'she will move heaven and earth to prevent our marriage. Say I am the sister of one of your fellow-servants – ask her to see me before you go into any more particulars – and leave it to me to do the rest. I want to make her love me next best to you, Isaac, before she knows anything of who I really am.'

The motive of the deceit was sufficient to **sanctify** it to Isaac. The stratagem proposed relieved him of his one great anxiety, and quieted his uneasy conscience on the subject of his mother. Still, there was something wanting to perfect his happiness, something that he could not realise, something mysteriously untraceable, and yet, something that perpetually made itself felt; not when he was absent from Rebecca Murdoch, but, strange to say, when he was actually in her presence! She was kindness itself with him; she never made him feel his inferior capacities, and inferior manners – she showed the sweetest anxiety to please him in the smallest trifles; but, in spite of all these attractions, he

infatuation: intense passion or love
faculties: mind
sanctify: justify

never could feel quite at his ease with her. At their first meeting, there had mingled with his admiration when he looked in her face, a faint involuntary feeling of doubt whether that face was entirely strange to him. No after familiarity had the slightest effect on this inexplicable, wearisome uncertainty.

Concealing the truth as he had been directed, he announced his marriage engagement **precipitately** and confusedly to his mother, on the day when he contracted it. Poor Mrs Scatchard showed her perfect confidence in her son by flinging her arms round his neck, and giving him joy of having found at last, in the sister of one of his fellow-servants, a woman to comfort and care for him after his mother was gone. She was all eagerness to see the woman of her son's choice; and the next day was fixed for the introduction.

It was a bright sunny morning, and the little cottage parlour was full of light, as Mrs Scatchard, happy and expectant, dressed for the occasion in her Sunday gown, sat waiting for her son and her future daughter-in-law. Punctual to the appointed time, Isaac hurriedly and nervously led his promised wife into the room. His mother rose to receive her – advanced a few steps, smiling – looked Rebecca full in the eyes – and suddenly stopped. Her face, which had been flushed the moment before, turned white in an instant – her eyes lost their expression of softness and kindness, and assumed a blank look of terror – her outstretched hands fell to her sides, and she staggered back a few steps with a low cry to her son.

'Isaac!' she whispered, clutching him fast by the arm, when he asked alarmingly if she was taken ill. 'Isaac! Does that woman's face remind you of nothing?'

Before he could answer; before he could look round to where Rebecca stood, at the lower end of the room; his mother pointed impatiently to her writing-desk, and gave him the key.

'Open it,' she said, in a quick, breathless whisper.

'What does this mean? Why am I treated as if I had no business here? Does your mother want to insult me?' asked Rebecca, angrily.

---

precipitately: hastily

'Open it, and give me the paper in the left-hand drawer. Quick! quick, for Heaven's Sake!' said Mrs Scatchard, shrinking further back in terror. Isaac gave her the paper. She looked it over eagerly for a moment – then followed Rebecca, who was now turning away haughtily to leave the room, and caught her by the shoulder – abruptly raised the long, loose sleeve of her gown, and glanced at her hand and arm. Something like fear began to steal over the angry expression of Rebecca's face as she shook herself free from the old woman's grasp. 'Mad!' she said to herself; 'and Isaac never told me.' With these few words she left the room.

Isaac was hastening after her when his mother turned and stopped his further progress. It wrung his heart to see the misery and terror in her face as she looked at him.

'Light grey eyes,' she said, in low, mournful, awe-struck tones, pointing towards the open door. 'A droop of the left eyelid. Flaxen hair with a gold-yellow streak in it. White arms with a down on them. Little, lady's hand, with a reddish look under the fingernails. *The woman of the dream!* – Oh, Heaven! Isaac, the woman of the dream!'

That faint **cleaving** doubt which he had never been able to shake off in Rebecca Murdoch's presence, was fatally set at rest for ever. He *had* seen her face, then, before – seven years before, on his birthday, in the bedroom of the lonely inn. 'The woman of the dream!'

'Be warned, Oh, my son! be warned! Isaac! let her go, and do you stop with me!'

Something darkened the parlour window, as those words were said. A sudden chill ran through him; and he glanced sidelong at the shadow. Rebecca Murdoch had come back. She was peering in curiously at them over the low window blind.

'I have promised to marry, mother,' he said, 'and marry I must.'

The tears came into his eyes as he spoke, and dimmed his sight; but he could just discern the fatal face outside moving away again from the window.

---

cleaving: nagging

His mother's head sank lower.

'Are you faint?' he whispered.

'Broken-hearted, Isaac.'

He stooped down and kissed her. The shadow, as he did so, returned to the window; and the fatal face peered in curiously once more.

Three weeks after that day, Isaac and Rebecca were man and wife. All that was hopelessly dogged and stubborn in the man's moral nature, seemed to have closed round his fatal passion, and to have fixed it **unassailably** in his heart.

After that first interview in the cottage parlour, no consideration would induce Mrs Scatchard to see her son's wife again, or even to talk of her when Isaac tried hard to plead her cause after their marriage. This course of conduct was not in any degree occasioned by a discovery of the **degradation** in which Rebecca had lived. There was no question of that between mother and son. There was no question of anything but the fearfully exact resemblance between the living breathing woman and the spectre woman of Isaac's dream. Rebecca, on her side, neither felt nor expressed the slightest sorrow at the estrangement between herself and her mother-in-law. Isaac, for the sake of peace, had never contradicted her first idea that age and long illness had affected Mrs Scatchard's mind. He even allowed his wife to **upbraid** him for not having confessed this to her at the time of their marriage engagement, rather than risk anything by hinting at the truth. The sacrifice of his integrity before his one all-mastering **delusion**, seemed but a small thing, and cost his conscience but little, after the sacrifices he had already made.

The time of waking from his delusion – the cruel and the rueful time – was not far off. After some quiet months of married life, as the summer was ending, and the year was getting on towards the month of his birthday, Isaac found his wife altering towards him. She grew sullen and contemptuous

---

unassailably: immovably
degradation: immorality
upbraid: criticise
delusion: self-deception

– she formed acquaintances of the most dangerous kind, in defiance of his objections, his **entreaties**, and his commands – and, worst of all, she learnt, ere long, after every fresh difference with her husband, to seek the deadly self-oblivion of drink. Little by little, after the first miserable discovery that his wife was keeping company with drunkards, the shocking certainty forced itself on Isaac that she had grown to be a drunkard herself.

He had been in a sadly **desponding** state for some time before the occurrence of these domestic calamities. His mother's health, as he could but too plainly discern every time he went to see her at the cottage, was failing fast; and he upbraided himself in secret as the cause of the bodily and mental suffering she endured. When, to his remorse on his mother's account, was added the shame and misery occasioned by the discovery of his wife's degradation, he sank under the double trial – his face began to alter fast, and he looked what he was, a spirit-broken man. His mother, still struggling bravely against the illness that was hurrying her to the grave, was the first to notice the sad alteration in him, and the first to hear of his last bitterest trouble with his wife. She could only weep bitterly, on the day when he made his humiliating confession; but on the next occasion when he went to see her, she had taken a resolution, in reference to his domestic afflictions, which astonished, and even alarmed him. He found her dressed to go out, and on asking the reason, received this answer:

'I am not long for this world, Isaac,' said she; 'and I shall not feel easy on my death-bed, unless I have done my best to the last, to make my son happy. I mean to put my own fears and my own feelings out of the question, and to go with you to your wife, and try what I can do to reclaim her. Give me your arm, Isaac; and let me do the last thing I can in this world to help my son before it is too late.'

He could not disobey her: and they walked together slowly towards his miserable home. It was only one o'clock in the

---

entreaties: pleas
desponding: despairing

afternoon when they reached the cottage where he lived. It was their dinner hour, and Rebecca was in the kitchen. He was thus able to take his mother quietly into the parlour, and then prepare his wife for the interview. She had fortunately drunk but little at that early hour, and she was less sullen and **capricious** than usual. He returned to his mother, with his mind tolerably at ease. His wife soon followed him into the parlour, and the meeting between her and Mrs Scatchard passed off better than he had ventured to anticipate: though he observed, with secret **apprehension**, that his mother, resolutely as she controlled herself in other respects, could not look his wife in the face when she spoke to her. It was a relief to him, therefore, when Rebecca began to lay the cloth.

She laid the cloth – brought in the bread-tray, and cut a slice from the loaf for her husband – then returned to the kitchen. At that moment, Isaac, still anxiously watching his mother, was startled by seeing the same ghastly change pass over her face, which had altered it so awfully on the morning when Rebecca and she first met. Before he could say a word she whispered with a look of horror:

'Take me back! – home, home, again, Isaac! Come with me, and never come back again.'

He was afraid to ask for an explanation – he could only sign to her to be silent, and help her quickly to the door. As they passed the bread-tray on the table she stopped and pointed to it.

'Did you see what your wife cut your bread with?' she asked, in a low, still whisper.

'No, mother – I was not noticing – what was it?'

'Look!'

He did look. A new clasp-knife, with a buck-horn handle lay with the loaf in the bread-tray. He stretched out his hand, shudderingly, to possess himself of it; but, at the same time, there was a noise in the kitchen, and his mother caught at his arm.

'The knife of the dream! – Isaac, I'm faint with fear – take me away! before she comes back!'

---

capricious: unpredictable
apprehension: anxiety

He was hardly able to support her – the visible **tangible** reality of the knife struck him with a panic, and utterly destroyed any faint doubts that he might have entertained up to this time, in relation to the mysterious dream-warning of nearly eight years before. By a last desperate effort, he summoned self-possession enough to help his mother quietly out of the house – so quietly, that the 'dream-woman' (he thought of her by that name, now!) did not hear them departing, from the kitchen.

'Don't go back, Isaac – don't go back!' implored Mrs Scatchard, as he turned to go away, after seeing her safely seated again in her own room.

'I must get the knife,' he answered under his breath. She tried to stop him again; but he hurried out without another word.

On his return, he found that his wife had discovered their secret departure from the house. She had been drinking, and was in a fury of passion. The dinner in the kitchen was flung under the grate; the cloth was off the parlour-table. Where was the knife? Unwisely, he asked for it. She was only too glad of the opportunity of irritating him, which the request afforded her. 'He wanted the knife, did he? Could he give her a reason why? – No! – Then he should not have it – not if he went down on his knees to ask for it.' Further **recriminations** elicited the fact that she had bought it a bargain – and that she considered it her own especial property. Isaac saw the uselessness of attempting to get the knife by fair means, and determined to search for it, later in the day, in secret. The search was unsuccessful. Night came on, and he left the house to walk about the streets. He was afraid now to sleep in the same room with her.

Three weeks passed. Still sullenly enraged with him, she would not give up the knife; and still that fear of sleeping in the same room with her, possessed him. He walked about at night, or dozed in the parlour, or sat watching by his mother's bedside. Before the **expiration** of the first week in the new

---

tangible: solid
recriminations: accusations
expiration: end

month his mother died. It wanted then but ten days of her son's birthday. She had longed to live till that anniversary. Isaac was present at her death; and her last words in this world were addressed to him: 'Don't go back, my son, don't go back!'

He was obliged to go back, if it were only to watch his wife. Exasperated to the last degree by his distrust of her, she had revengefully sought to add a sting to his grief, during the last days of his mother's illness, by declaring that she would assert her right to attend the funeral. In spite of all that he could do, or say, she held with wicked **pertinacity** to her word; and, on the day appointed for the burial, forced herself – inflamed and shameless with drink – into her husband's presence, and declared that she would walk in the funeral procession to his mother's grave.

The last worst outrage, accompanied by all that was most insulting in word and look, maddened him for the moment. He struck her. The instant the blow was dealt, he repented it. She crouched down, silent in a corner of the room, and eyed him steadily; it was a look that cooled his hot blood, and made him tremble. But there was no time now to think of a means of making **atonement**. Nothing remained but to risk the worst till the funeral was over. There was but one way of making sure of her. He locked her into her bedroom.

When he came back some hours after, he found her sitting, very much altered in look and bearing, by the bedside with a bundle on her lap. She rose, and faced him quietly, and spoke with a strange stillness in her voice, a strange repose in her eyes, a strange composure in her manner.

'No man has ever struck me twice,' she said, 'and my husband shall have no second opportunity. Set the door open and let me go. From this day forth we see each other no more.'

Before he could answer she passed him, and left the room. He saw her walk away up the street.

Would she return? All that night he watched and waited; but no footstep came near the house. The next night, overpowered by fatigue, he lay down in bed, in his clothes, with the door

pertinacity: obstinacy
atonement: amends

locked, the key on the table, and the candle burning. His slumber was not disturbed. The third night, the fourth, the fifth, the sixth, passed, and nothing happened. He lay down on the seventh, still in his clothes, still with the door locked, the key on the table, and the candle burning, but easier in his mind.

Easier in his mind, and in perfect health of body, when he fell off to sleep. But his rest was disturbed. He woke twice, without any sensation of uneasiness. But the third time it was that never-to-be-forgotten shivering of the night at the lonely inn, that dreadful sinking pain at the heart, which once more aroused him in an instant.

His eyes opened towards the left hand side of the bed and there stood – The woman of the dream, again? – No! His wife; the living reality, with the dream-spectre's face – in the dream-spectre's attitude; the fair arm up – the knife clasped in the delicate, white hand.

He sprang upon her, almost at the instant of seeing her, and yet not quickly enough to prevent her from hiding the knife. Without a word from him – without a cry from her – he pinioned her in a chair. With one hand he felt up her sleeve – and, there, where the dream-woman had hidden the knife, she had hidden it – the knife with the buck-horn handle, that looked like new.

In the despair of that fearful moment his brain was steady, his heart was calm. He looked at her fixedly, with the knife in his hand, and said these last words:

'You told me we should see each other no more, and you have come back. It is my turn, now, to go, and to go for ever. *I* say that we shall see each other no more; and *my* word shall not be broken.'

He left her, and set forth into the night. There was a bleak wind abroad, and the smell of recent rain was in the air. The distant church clocks chimed the quarter as he walked rapidly beyond the last houses in the suburb. He asked the first policeman he met, what hour that was, of which the quarter had just struck.

The man referred sleepily to his watch, and answered: 'Two o'clock.' Two in the morning. What day of the month was this day that had just begun? He reckoned it up from the date of his mother's funeral. The fatal parallel was complete – it was his birthday!

Had he escaped the mortal peril which his dream foretold? or had he only received a second warning? As that ominous doubt forced itself on his mind, he stopped, reflected, and turned back again towards the city. He was still resolute to hold to his word, and never to let her see him more; but there was a thought now in his mind of having her watched and followed. The knife was in his possession – the world was before him; but a new distrust of her – a vague, unspeakable, superstitious dread – had overcome him.

'I must know where she goes, now she thinks I have left her,' he said to himself, as he stole back wearily to the precincts of his house.

It was still dark. He had left the candle burning in the bedchamber: but when he looked up at the window of the room now, there was no light in it. He crept cautiously to the house-door. On going away, he remembered to have closed it: on trying it now, he found it open.

He waited outside, never losing sight of the house, till daylight. Then he ventured indoors – listened, and heard nothing – looked into kitchen, scullery, parlour; and found nothing: went up, at last, into the bedroom – it was empty. A pick-lock lay on the floor, betraying how she had gained entrance in the night; and that was the only trace of her.

Whither had she gone? That no mortal tongue could tell him. The darkness had covered her flight; and when the day broke, no man could say where the light found her.

Before leaving the house and the town for ever, he gave instructions to a friend and neighbour to sell his furniture for anything that it would fetch, and apply the proceeds to employing the police to trace her. The directions were honestly followed, and the money was all spent; but the inquiries led to nothing. The pick-lock on the bedroom floor remained the last useless trace of her.

* * *

At this point of the narrative the landlord paused, and looked towards the stable-door.

'So far,' he said, 'I tell you what was told to me. The little that remains to be added lies within my own experience. Between two and three months after the events I have just been relating, Isaac Scatchard came to me, withered and old-looking before his time, just as you saw him today. He had his testimonials to character with him, and he asked for employment here. I gave him a trial and liked him in spite of his queer habits. He is as sober, honest, and willing a man as there is in England. As for his restlessness at night, and his sleeping away his leisure time in the day, who can wonder at it after hearing his story? Besides, he never objects to being roused up, when he's wanted, so there's not much inconvenience to complain of, after all.'

'I suppose he is afraid of waking out of that dreadful dream in the dark?' said I.

'No,' returned the landlord. 'The dream comes back to him so often, that he has got to bear with it by this time resignedly enough. It's his wife keeps him waking at night, as he has often told me.'

'What! Has she never been heard of yet?'

'Never. Isaac himself has the one perpetual thought about her, that she is alive and looking for him. I believe he wouldn't let himself drop off to sleep towards two in the morning for a king's ransom. Two in the morning, he says, is the time when she will find him, one of these days. Two in the morning is the time all the year round, when he likes to be most certain that he has got that clasp-knife safe about him. He does not mind being alone, as long as he is awake except on the night before his birthday, when he firmly believes himself to be in peril of his life. The birthday has only come once since he has been here; and then he sat up, along with the night-porter. "She's looking for me," he always says, when I speak to him on the one theme of his life; "she's looking for me." He may be right. She *may* be looking for him. Who can tell?'

'Who can tell!' said I.

Non-fiction passages linked to
The Ostler (1855)

Wilkie Collins's own phantoms

Like Isaac, Collins himself was used to ghostly 'visitations':

He spoke openly to his friends of ghosts standing behind him, and of a green woman with teeth like tusks who appeared on the stairs, along with other ghosts, 'trying to push him down'. He also spoke of 'another Wilkie Collins' appearing before him if and when he worked into the night. As the story goes, 'the second Wilkie Collins sat at the same table with him and tried to monopolise the writing pad. Then there was a struggle, and the inkstand was upset; anyhow, when the true Wilkie awoke, the inkstand had been upset and the ink was running over the writing table.'

William M. Clarke, 1988

Dreams foretelling the future

a Isaac's dream at the inn turns out to predict his future relationship with Rebecca. Such dreams are described as 'precognitive' (that is, 'knowing in advance'):

PRECOGNITIVE **DREAMS** are a special case of ESP [extrasensory perception]. As the name suggests, in precognitive dreams the dreamer experiences an event, in whole or in part, before it occurs. It has been suggested that at least some experiences of déja vù – the uncanny sense that a completely unknown place is familiar, as if one had been there before, or that a new situation has been experienced before – can be explained by precognitive dreams.

James R. Lewis, 1995

b Isaac's 'dream-woman' has long fair hair and wields a knife. How accurately does this foretell his future, according to traditional dream symbolism?

Hair. If you imagine you see a strange woman with long and beautiful hair, it is a very good sign as it denotes friendship, joy and prosperity.

Knife. To dream of knives is a very unpropitious omen. It signifies law-suits, poverty, disgrace, strife and failure.

From *The Classic 1000 Dreams, 1991*

Nightmares about one's own death

There are many true-life stories of people suffering nightmares that predict their own death, as Isaac does. One of the strangest concerns President Lincoln:

Legend says that American President Abraham Lincoln had a strong belief in ghosts: he apparently consulted a medium during the worst days of the Civil War and, according to W. H. Crook, one of his bodyguards, Lincoln had a number of psychic experiences. At the beginning of April 1865, he told Crook that he had had a dream in which he had been in the hall of the White House, and had seen a coffin draped in black there. When he asked who it was for, he was told: 'The president.'

On 11 April, Lincoln told Crook that he had dreamed of his own assassination; and on the morning of 14 April he had a vision of a ship carrying him to some unknown place. That night, against the advice of Crook and other members of his staff, Lincoln went to Ford's Theater in Washington. There he was shot dead by John Wilkes Booth. Within months of Lincoln's death, rumours began to circulate that his ghost was haunting the White House.

Reuben Stine, 1993

Confession Found in a Prison
Charles Dickens

I held a lieutenant's **commission** in His Majesty's army and served abroad in the campaigns of 1677 and 1678. The treaty of Nimeguen being concluded, I returned home, and retiring from the service withdrew to a small estate lying a few miles east of London, which I had recently acquired in right of my wife.

This is the last night I have to live, and I will set down the naked truth without disguise. I was never a brave man, and had always been from my childhood of a secret sullen distrustful nature. I speak of myself as if I had passed from the world, for while I write this my grave is digging and my name is written in the black book of death.

Soon after my return to England, my only brother was seized with mortal illness. This circumstance gave me slight or no pain, for since we had been men we had associated but very little together. He was open-hearted and generous, handsomer than I, more accomplished, and generally beloved. Those who sought my acquaintance abroad or at home because they were friends of his, seldom attached themselves to me long, and would usually say in our first conversation that they were surprised to find two brothers so unlike in their manners and appearance. It was my habit to lead them on to this avowal, for I knew what comparisons they must draw between us, and having a **rankling** envy in my heart, I sought to justify it to myself.

We had married two sisters. This additional tie between us, as it may appear to some, only estranged us the more. His wife knew me well. I never struggled with any secret jealousy or **gall** when she was present but that woman knew it as well as I did.

commission: rank
rankling: aching, painful
gall: bitterness

I never raised my eyes at such times but I found hers fixed upon me; I never bent them on the ground or looked another way, but I felt that she overlooked me always. It was an inexpressible relief to me when we quarrelled, and a greater relief still when I heard abroad that she was dead. It seems to me now as if some strange and terrible **foreshadowing** of what has happened since, must have hung over us then. I was afraid of her, she haunted me, her fixed and steady look comes back upon me now like the memory of a dark dream and makes my blood run cold.

She died shortly after giving birth to a child – a boy. When my brother knew that all hope of his own recovery was past, he called my wife to his bed-side and confided this orphan, a child of four years old, to her protection. He **bequeathed** to him all the property he had, and willed that in case of the child's death it should pass to my wife as the only acknowledgement he could make her for her care and love. He exchanged a few brotherly words with me deploring our long separation, and being exhausted, fell into a slumber from which he never awoke.

We had no children, and as there had been a strong affection between the sisters, and my wife had almost supplied the place of a mother to this boy, she loved him as if he had been her own. The child was **ardently** attached to her; but he was his mother's image in face and spirit and always mistrusted me.

I can scarcely fix the date when the feeling first came upon me, but I soon began to be uneasy when this child was by. I never roused myself from some moody train of thought but I marked him looking at me: not with mere childish wonder, but with something of the purpose and meaning that I had so often noted in his mother. It was no effort of my **fancy**, founded on close resemblance of feature and expression. I never could look the boy down. He feared me, but seemed by some instinct to despise me while he did so; and even when he drew back beneath my

foreshadowing: premonition
bequeathed: left in his will
ardently: strongly and lovingly
fancy: imagination

gaze – as he would when we were alone, to get nearer to the door – he would keep his bright eyes upon me still.

Perhaps I hide the truth from myself, but I do not think that when this began, I **meditated** to do him any wrong. I may have thought how serviceable his inheritance would be to us, and may have wished him dead, but I believe I had no thought of **compassing** his death. Neither did the idea come upon me at once, but by very slow degrees, presenting itself at first in dim shapes at a very great distance, as men may think of an earthquake or the last day – then drawing nearer and nearer and losing something of its horror and improbability – then coming to be part and parcel, nay nearly the whole sum and substance of my daily thoughts, and resolving itself into a question of means and safety; not of doing or abstaining from the deed.

While this was going on with me, I never could bear that the child should see me looking at him, and yet I was under a fascination which made it a kind of business with me to contemplate his slight and fragile figure and think how easily it might be done. Sometimes I would steal upstairs and watch him as he slept, but usually I hovered in the garden near the window of the room in which he learnt his little tasks, and there as he sat upon a low seat beside my wife, I would peer at him for hours together from behind a tree: starting like the guilty wretch I was at every rustling of a leaf, and still gliding back to look and start again.

Hard by our cottage, but quite out of sight, and (if there were any wind astir) of hearing too, was a deep sheet of water. I spent days in shaping with my pocket-knife a rough model of a boat, which I finished at last and dropped in the child's way. Then I withdrew to a secret place which he must pass if he stole away alone to **swim this bauble**, and lurked there for his coming. He came neither that day nor the next, though I waited from noon till nightfall. I was sure that I had him in my net for I had heard him from prattling of the toy, and knew that in his

---

meditated: planned
compassing: causing
swim this bauble: sail this plaything (i.e. the toy boat)

infant pleasure he kept it by his side in bed. I felt no weariness or fatigue, but waited patiently, and on the third day he passed me, running joyously along, with his silken hair streaming in the wind and he singing – God have mercy upon me! – singing a merry ballad – who could hardly lisp the words.

I stole down after him, creeping under certain shrubs which grow in that place, and none but devils know with what terror I, a full-grown man, tracked the footsteps of that baby as he approached the water's brink. I was close upon him, had sunk upon my knee and raised my hand to thrust him in, when he saw my shadow in the stream and turned him round.

His mother's ghost was looking from his eyes. The sun burst forth from behind a cloud: it shone in the bright sky, the glistening earth, the clear water, the sparkling drops of rain upon the leaves. There were eyes in everything. The whole great universe of light was there to see the murder done. I know not what he said; he came of bold and manly blood, and child as he was, he did not crouch or fawn upon me. I heard him cry that he would try to love me – not that he did – and then I saw him running back towards the house. The next I saw was my own sword naked in my hand and he lying at my feet stark dead – dabbled here and there with blood but otherwise no different from what I had seen him in his sleep – in the same **attitude** too, with his cheek resting upon his little hand.

I took him in my arms and laid him – very gently now that he was dead – in a thicket. My wife was from home that day and would not return until the next. Our bed-room window, the only sleeping room on that side of the house, was but a few feet from the ground, and I resolved to descend from it at night and bury him in the garden. I had no thought that I had failed in my design, no thought that the water would be dragged and nothing found, that the money must now lie waste since I must encourage the idea that the child was lost or stolen. All my thoughts were bound up and knotted together, in the one absorbing necessity of hiding what I had done.

---

attitude: position

How I felt when they came to tell me that the child was missing, when I ordered **scouts** in all directions, when I gasped and trembled at everyone's approach, no tongue can tell or mind of man conceive. I buried him that night. When I parted the boughs and looked into the dark thicket, there was a glow-worm shining like the visible spirit of God upon the murdered child. I glanced down into his grave when I had placed him there and still it gleamed upon his breast: an eye of fire looking up to Heaven in **supplication** to the stars that watched me at my work.

I had to meet my wife, and break the news, and give her hope that the child would soon be found. All this I did – with some appearance, I suppose, of being sincere, for I was the object of no suspicion. This done, I sat at the bed-room window all day long and watched the spot where the dreadful secret lay.

It was in a piece of ground which had been dug up to be newly turfed, and which I had chosen on that account as the traces of my spade were less likely to attract attention. The men who laid down the grass must have thought me mad. I called to them continually to **expedite** their work, ran out and worked beside them, trod down the turf with my feet, and hurried them with frantic eagerness. They had finished their task before night, and then I thought myself comparatively safe.

I slept – not as men do who wake refreshed and cheerful, but I did sleep, passing from vague and shadowy dreams of being hunted down, to visions of the plot of grass, through which now a hand and now a foot and now the head itself was starting out. At this point I always woke and stole to the window to make sure that it was not really so. That done I crept to bed again, and thus I spent the night in fits and starts, getting up and lying down full twenty times and dreaming the same dream over and over again – which was far worse than lying awake, for every dream had a whole night's suffering of its own. Once I thought the child was alive and that I had never tried to kill him. To wake from that dream was the most dreadful agony of all.

---

scouts: searchers
supplication: prayer
expedite: speed up

The next day I sat at the window again, never once taking my eyes from the place, which, although it was covered by the grass, was as plain to me – its shape, its size, its depth, its jagged sides, and all – as if it had been open to the light of day. When a servant walked across it, I felt as if he must sink in; when he had passed I looked to see that his feet had not worn the edges. If a bird lighted there, I was in terror lest by some tremendous **interposition** it should be instrumental in the discovery; if a breath of air sighed across it, to me it whispered murder. There was not a sight or sound how ordinary mean or unimportant soever, but was fraught with fear. And in this state of ceaseless watching I spent three days.

On the fourth, there came to the gate one who had served with me abroad, accompanied by a brother officer of his whom I had never seen. I felt that I could not bear to be out of sight of the place. It was a summer evening, and I bade my people take a table and a flask of wine into the garden. Then I sat down *with my chair upon the grave*, and being assured that nobody could disturb it now, without my knowledge, tried to drink and talk.

They hoped that my wife was well – that she was not obliged to **keep her chamber** – that they had not frightened her away. What could I do but tell them with a faltering tongue about the child? The officer whom I did not know was a down-looking man and kept his eyes upon the ground while I was speaking. Even that terrified me! I could not divest myself of the idea that he saw something which caused him to suspect the truth. I asked him hurriedly if he supposed that – and stopped. 'That the child had been murdered?' said he, looking mildly at me. 'Oh, no! what could a man gain by murdering a poor child?' *I* could have told him what a man gained by such a deed, no one better, but I held my peace and shivered as with an **ague**.

Mistaking my emotion they were endeavouring to cheer me with the hope that the boy would certainly be found – great cheer that was for me – when we heard a low deep howl, and

interposition: chance
keep her chamber: stay in her bedroom
ague: fever

presently there sprung over the wall two great dogs, who bounding into the garden repeated the baying sound we had heard before.

'Blood-hounds!' cried my visitors.

What need to tell me that! I had never seen one of that kind in all my life, but I knew what they were and for what purpose they had come. I grasped the elbows of my chair, and neither spoke nor moved.

'They are of the **genuine breed**,' said the man whom I had known abroad, 'and being out for exercise have no doubt escaped from their keeper.'

Both he and his friend turned to look at the dogs, who with their noses to the ground moved restlessly about, running to and fro, and up and down, and across, and round in circles, careering about like wild things, and all this time taking no notice of us, but ever and again lifting their heads and repeating the yell we had heard already, then dropping their noses to the ground again and tracking earnestly here and there. They now began to snuff the earth more eagerly than they had done yet, and although they were still very restless, no longer beat about in such wide circuits, but kept near to one spot, and constantly diminished the distance between themselves and me.

At last they came up close to the great chair on which I sat, and raising their frightful howl once more, tried to tear away the wooden rails that kept them from the ground beneath. I saw how I looked, in the faces of the two who were with me.

'They scent some prey,' said they, both together.

'They scent no prey!' cried I.

'In Heaven's name move,' said the one I knew, very earnestly, 'or you will be torn to pieces.'

'Let them tear me limb from limb, I'll never leave this place!' cried I. 'Are dogs to hurry men to shameful deaths? Hew them down, cut them in pieces.'

'There is some foul mystery here!' said the officer whom I did not know, drawing his sword. 'In King Charles's name assist me to secure this man.'

---

genuine breed: pedigree stock

They both set upon me and forced me away, though I fought and bit and caught at them like a madman. After a struggle they got me quietly between them, and then, my God! I saw the angry dogs tearing at the earth and throwing it up into the air like water.

What more have I to tell? That I fell upon my knees and with chattering teeth confessed the truth and prayed to be forgiven. That I have since denied and now confess to it again. That I have been tried for the crime, found guilty, and sentenced. That I have not the courage to anticipate my doom or to bear up manfully against it. That I have no compassion, no consolation, no hope, no friend. That my wife has happily lost for the time those faculties which would enable her to know my misery or hers. That I am alone in this stone dungeon with my evil spirit, and that I die to-morrow!

Non-fiction passages linked to *Confession Found in a Prison* (1842)

Literary background: the influence of Edgar Allan Poe

Confession Found in a Prison is Dickens's attempt to write in the vein of the American author Edgar Allan Poe (1809–1849). Poe was a master of the Gothic horror story. He has influenced almost every horror writer since, from Bram Stoker (*Dracula*) to Stephen King in the present day:

a The typical ingredients of Poe's fiction are the same as those in Dickens's story: violence, brutal murder, sensationalism, and characters who suffer from mad or deranged states of mind. Two of the most spine-chilling are *The Pit and the Pendulum* and *The Fall of the House of Usher*.

b There are strong similarities between *Confession Found in a Prison* and Poe's horror story *The Tell-Tale Heart*. Both central characters are 'driven' to commit murder without clear motive. Both try desperately to hide their crime: in Poe's story, the body is concealed beneath the floor-boards. Both are suspected and finally confess: in Poe's story, the murderer breaks down when he is convinced his victim's heart is still beating and can he heard echoing around the house.

c Dickens and Poe admired each other's work. Poe wrote a complimentary review of *Confession Found in a Prison*, describing it as 'a paper [story] of remarkable power' (*Graham's Magazine*).

Mike Royston, 2002

Possession by evil spirits

The narrator describes himself in the condemned cell as 'alone . . . with my evil spirit' (page 155). For Dickens this was not just a figure of speech. He believed in possession by evil. Moreover, he believed that he himself could cure it by hypnotising the person possessed. The Victorians called this 'mesmerism':

> His most extensive experience as a mesmeric operator began during his Italian stay in Genoa in 1844, with his English-born Swiss friend Madame Emile de la Rue, who suffered from a number of symptoms, including a nervous tic, convulsions, headaches and insomnia. He treated her over a period of years, believing that he was struggling for control of her psyche with a sinister evil phantom.

Paul Schlicke, 1999

The Evil Eye

As he murders his nephew, the narrator says: 'His mother's ghost was looking from his eyes . . . There were eyes in everything' (page 151). The power of the Evil Eye to cast a curse on wrongdoers has a long history:

> **IN** earlier times it was believed that there is such a thing as an eye-beam; a potent influence emitted from every eye; and that evil-minded folk could manipulate and intensify their eye-beams to wreak havoc and harm ... The eye was associated with Satan, a leader of angels or stars, the 'eyes' of the night sky. So the peacock is connected with Satan due to the 'eyes' on its tail, while in modern occult symbolism the Devil is linked with the Hebrew letter *ayin*, traditionally representing an eye.

Stuart Gordon, 1997

The Red Room
H. G. Wells

'I can assure you,' said I, 'that it will take a very **tangible** ghost to frighten me.' And I stood up before the fire with my glass in my hand.

'It is your own choosing,' said the man with the withered arm, and glanced at me askance.

'Eight-and-twenty years,' said I, 'I have lived, and never a ghost have I seen as yet.'

The old woman sat staring hard into the fire, her pale eyes wide open. 'Ay,' she broke in; 'and eight-and-twenty years you have lived and never seen the likes of this house, I reckon. There's a many things to see, when one's still but eight-and-twenty.' She swayed her head slowly from side to side. 'A many things to see the sorrow for.'

I half-suspected the old people were trying to **enhance** the spiritual terrors of their house by their droning insistence. I put down my empty glass on the table and looked about the room, and caught the glimpse of myself, abbreviated and broadened to an impossible sturdiness, in the queer old mirror at the end of the room. 'Well,' I said, 'if I see anything tonight, I shall be so much the wiser. For I come to the business with an open mind.'

'It's your own choosing,' said the man with the withered arm once more.

I heard the sound of a stick and a shambling step on the flags in the passage outside, and the door creaked on its hinges as a second old man entered, more bent, more wrinkled, more aged even than the first. He supported himself by a single crutch, his eyes were covered by a shade, and his lower lip, half-averted, hung pale and pink from his decaying yellow teeth. He made straight for an armchair on the opposite side of the table, sat down clumsily, and began to cough. The man with the

tangible: solid
enhance: add to

withered arm gave this newcomer a short glance of positive dislike; the old woman took no notice of his arrival, but remained with her eyes fixed steadily on the fire.

'I said – it's your own choosing,' said the man with the withered arm, when the coughing had ceased for a while.

'It's my own choosing,' I answered.

The man with the shade became aware of my presence for the first time, and threw his head back for a moment and sideways, to see me. I caught a momentary glimpse of his eyes, small and bright and inflamed. Then he began to cough and splutter again.

'Why don't you drink?' said the man with the withered arm, pushing the beer towards him. The man with the shade poured out a glassful with a shaky arm that splashed half as much again on the deal table. A monstrous shadow of him crouched upon the wall and mocked his action as he poured and drank. I must confess I had scarce expected these **grotesque custodians**. There is to my mind something inhuman in senility, something crouching and **atavistic**; the human qualities seem to drop from old people insensibly day by day. The three of them made me feel uncomfortable, with their gaunt silences, their bent **carriage**, their evident unfriendliness to me and to one another.

'If,' said I, 'you will show me to this haunted room of yours, I will make myself comfortable there.'

The old man with the cough jerked his head back so suddenly that it startled me, and shot another glance of his red eyes at me from under the shade; but no one answered me. I waited a minute, glancing from one to the other.

'If,' I said a little louder, 'if you will show me to this haunted room of yours, I will relieve you from the task of entertaining me.'

'There's a candle on the slab outside the door,' said the man with the withered arm, looking at my feet as he addressed me. 'But if you go to the red room tonight' –

---

grotesque custodians: ugly servants
atavistic: ancient looking
carriage: posture

('This night of all nights!' said the old woman.)

'You go alone.'

'Very well,' I answered. 'And which way do I go?'

'You go along the passage for a bit,' said he, 'until you come to a door, and through that is a spiral staircase, and half-way up that is a landing and another door covered with baize. Go through that and down the long corridor to the end, and the red room is on your left up the steps.'

'Have I got that right?' I said, and repeated his directions. He corrected me in one particular.

'And you are really going?' said the man with the shade, looking at me again for the third time, with that queer, unnatural tilting of the face.

('This night of all nights!' said the old woman.)

'It is what I came for,' I said, and moved towards the door. As I did so, the old man with the shade rose and staggered round the table, so as to be closer to the others and to the fire. At the door I turned and looked at them, and saw they were all close together, dark against the firelight, staring at me over their shoulders, with an intent expression on their ancient faces.

'Good-night,' I said, setting the door open.

'It's your own choosing,' said the man with the withered arm.

I left the door wide open until the candle was well alight, and then I shut them in and walked down the chilly, echoing passage.

I must confess that the oddness of these three old pensioners in whose charge her ladyship had left the castle, and the deep-toned, old-fashioned furniture of the housekeeper's room in which they foregathered, affected me in spite of my efforts to keep myself at a matter-of-fact phase. They seemed to belong to another age, an older age, an age when things spiritual were different from this of ours, less certain; an age when omens and witches were credible, and ghosts beyond denying. Their very existence was spectral; the cut of their clothing, fashions born in dead brains. The ornaments and **conveniences** of the room about them were

---

conveniences: furnishings

ghostly – the thoughts of vanished men, which still haunted rather than participated in the world of today. But with an effort I sent such thoughts to the right-about. The long, draughty subterranean passage was chilly and dusty, and my candle flared and made the shadows cower and quiver. The echoes rang up and down the spiral staircase, and a shadow came sweeping up after me, and one fled before me into the darkness overhead. I came to the landing and stopped there for a moment, listening to a rustling that I fancied I heard; then, satisfied of the absolute silence, I pushed open the baize-covered door and stood in the corridor.

The effect was scarcely what I expected, for the moonlight, coming in by the great window on the grand staircase, picked out everything in vivid black shadow or silvery illumination. Everything was in its place: the house might have been deserted on the yesterday instead of eighteen months ago. There were candles in the sockets of the **sconces**, and whatever dust had gathered on the carpets or upon the polished flooring was distributed so evenly as to be invisible in the moonlight. I was about to advance, and stopped abruptly. A bronze **group** stood upon the landing, hidden from me by the corner of the wall, but its shadow fell with marvellous distinctness upon the white panelling, and gave me the impression of someone crouching to waylay me. I stood rigid for half a minute perhaps. Then, with my hand in the pocket that held my revolver, I advanced, only to discover a Ganymede and Eagle glistening in the moonlight. That incident for a time restored my nerve, and a porcelain Chinaman on a **buhl** table, whose head rocked silently as I passed him, scarcely startled me.

The door to the red room and the steps up to it were in a shadowy corner. I moved my candle from side to side, in order to see clearly the nature of the recess in which I stood before opening the door. Here it was, thought I, that my predecessor was found, and the memory of that story gave me a sudden twinge of apprehension. I glanced over my shoulder at the

---

sconces: candle-holders set into the wall
group: a statue of the classical figures Ganymede and the Eagle
buhl: ornamental

Ganymede in the moonlight, and opened the door of the red room rather hastily, with my face half turned to the pallid silence of the landing.

I entered, closed the door behind me at once, turned the key I found in the lock within, and stood with the candle held aloft, surveying the scene of my vigil, the great red room of Lorraine Castle, in which the young duke had died. Or, rather, in which he had begun his dying, for he had opened the door and fallen headlong down the steps I had just ascended. That had been the end of his vigil, of his gallant attempt to conquer the ghostly tradition of the place; and never, I thought, had **apoplexy** better served the ends of superstition. And there were other and older stories that clung to the room, back to the half-credible beginning of it all, the tale of a timid wife and the tragic end that came to her husband's jest of frightening her. And looking around that large shadowy room, with its shadowy window bays, its recesses and alcoves, one could well understand the legends that had sprouted in its black corners, its germinating darkness. My candle was a little tongue of flame in its vastness, that failed to pierce the opposite end of the room, and left an ocean of mystery and suggestion beyond its island of light.

I resolved to make a systematic examination of the place at once, and dispel the fanciful suggestions of its obscurity before they obtained a hold upon me. After satisfying myself of the fastening of the door, I began to walk about the room, peering round each article of furniture, tucking up the **valances** of the bed, and opening its curtains wide. I pulled up the blinds and examined the fastenings of the several windows before closing the shutters, leant forward and looked up the blackness of the wide chimney, and tapped the dark oak panelling for any secret opening. There were two big mirrors in the room, each with a pair of sconces bearing candles, and on the mantelshelf, too, were more candles in china candlesticks. And these I lit one after the other. The fire was laid, – an unexpected consideration from the old housekeeper, – and I lit it, to keep

apoplexy: a sudden stroke
valances: hangings on the bedframe to hide the space beneath it

down any disposition to shiver, and when it was burning well, I stood round with my back to it and regarded the room again. I had pulled up a chintz-covered armchair and a table, to form a kind of barricade before me, and on this lay my revolver ready to hand. My precise examination had done me good, but I still found the remoter darkness of the place, and its perfect stillness, too stimulating for the imagination. The echoing of the stir and crackling of the fire was no sort of comfort to me. The shadow in the alcove, at the end in particular, had that undefinable quality of a presence, that odd suggestion of a lurking living thing, that comes so easily in silence and solitude. At last, to reassure myself, I walked with a candle into it, and satisfied myself that there was nothing tangible there. I stood that candle upon the floor of the alcove, and left it in that position.

By this time I was in a state of considerable nervous tension, although to my reason there was no adequate cause for the condition. My mind, however, was perfectly clear. I postulated quite unreservedly that nothing supernatural could happen, and to pass the time I began to string some rhymes together, **Ingoldsby fashion**, of the original legend of the place. A few I spoke aloud, but the echoes were not pleasant. For the same reason I also abandoned, after a time, a conversation with myself upon the impossibility of ghosts and haunting. My mind reverted to the three old and distorted people downstairs, and I tried to keep it upon that topic. The sombre reds and blacks of the room troubled me; even with seven candles the place was merely dim. The one in the alcove flared in a draught, and the fire-flickering kept the shadows and **penumbra** perpetually shifting and stirring. Casting about for a remedy, I recalled the candles I had seen in the passage, and, with a slight effort, walked out into the moonlight, carrying a candle and leaving the door open, and presently returned with as many as ten. These I put in various knick-knacks of china with which the room was sparsely

---

Ingoldsby fashion: in the style of *The Ingoldsby Legends*, a collection of nineteenth-century ghost poems
penumbra: half-shadows

adorned, lit and placed where the shadows had lain deepest, some on the floor, some in the window recesses, until at last my seventeen candles were so arranged that not an inch of the room but had the direct light of at least one of them. It occurred to me that when the ghost came, I could warn him not to trip over them. The room was now quite brightly illuminated. There was something very cheery and reassuring in these little streaming flames, and snuffing them gave me an occupation, and afforded a reassuring sense of the passage of time.

Even with that, however, the brooding expectation of the vigil weighed heavily upon me. It was after midnight that the candle in the alcove suddenly went out, and the black shadow sprang back to its place. I did not see the candle go out; I simply turned and saw that the darkness was there, as one might start and see the unexpected presence of a stranger. 'By Jove!' said I aloud; 'that draught's a strong one!' and, taking the matches from the table, I walked across the room in a leisurely manner to relight the corner again. My first match would not strike, and as I succeeded with the second, something seemed to blink on the wall before me. I turned my head involuntarily, and saw that the two candles on the little table by the fireplace were extinguished. I rose at once to my feet.

'Odd!' I said. 'Did I do that myself in a flash of absent-mindedness?'

I walked back, relit one, and as I did so, I saw the candle in the right sconce of one of the mirrors wink and go right out, and almost immediately its companion followed it. There was no mistake about it. The flame vanished, as if the wicks had been suddenly nipped between a finger and a thumb, leaving the wick neither glowing nor smoking, but black. Whilst I stood gaping, the candle at the foot of the bed went out, and the shadows seemed to take another step towards me.

'This won't do!' said I, and first one and then another candle on the mantelshelf followed.

'What's up?' I cried, with a queer high note getting into my voice somehow. At that the candle on the wardrobe went out, and the one I had relit in the alcove followed.

'Steady on!' I said. 'These candles are wanted,' speaking with a half-hysterical **facetiousness**, and scratching away at a match the while for the mantel candlesticks. My hands trembled so much that twice I missed the rough paper of the matchbox. As the mantel emerged from darkness again, two candles in the remoter end of the window were eclipsed. But with the same match I also relit the larger mirror candles, and those on the floor near the doorway, so that for the moment I seemed to gain on the extinctions. But then in a volley there vanished four lights at once in different corners of the room, and I struck another match in quivering haste, and stood hesitating whither to take it.

As I stood undecided, an invisible hand seemed to sweep out the two candles on the table. With a cry of terror, I dashed at the alcove, then into the corner, and then into the window, relighting three, as two more vanished by the fireplace; then, perceiving a better way, I dropped the matches on the iron-bound deed-box in the corner, and caught up the bedroom candlestick. With this I avoided the delay of striking matches; but for all that the steady process of extinction went on, and the shadows I feared and fought again returned, and crept in upon me, first a step gained on this side of me and then on that. It was like a ragged storm-cloud sweeping out the stars. Now and then one returned for a minute, and was lost again. I was now almost frantic with the horror of coming darkness, and my self-possession deserted me. I leaped panting and dishevelled from candle to candle, in a vain struggle against that remorseless advance.

I bruised myself on the thigh against the table, I sent a chair headlong, I stumbled and fell and whisked the cloth from the table in my fall. My candle rolled away from me, and I snatched another as I rose. Abruptly this was blown out, as I swung it off the table, by the wind of my sudden movement, and immediately the two remaining candles followed. But there was light still in the room, a red light that staved off the shadows from me. The fire! Of course, I could thrust my candle between the bars and relight it!

---

facetiousness: jokiness

I turned to where the flames were dancing between the glowing coals, and splashing red reflections upon the furniture, made two steps towards the grate, and **incontinently** the flames dwindled and vanished, the glow vanished, the reflections rushed together and vanished, and as I thrust the candle between the bars, darkness closed upon me like the shutting of an eye, wrapped about me in a stifling embrace, sealed my vision, and crushed the last vestiges of reason from my brain. The candle fell from my hand. I flung out my arms in a vain effort to thrust that ponderous blackness away from me, and, lifting up my voice, screamed with all my might – once, twice, thrice. Then I think I must have staggered to my feet. I know I thought suddenly of the moonlit corridor, and, with my head bowed and my arms over my face, made a run for the door.

But I had forgotten the exact position of the door, and struck myself heavily against the corner of the bed. I staggered back, turned, and was either struck or struck myself against some other bulky furniture. I have a vague memory of battering myself thus, to and fro in the darkness, of a cramped struggle, and of my own wild crying as I darted to and fro, of a heavy blow at last upon my forehead, a horrible sensation of falling that lasted an age, of my last frantic effort to keep my footing, and then I remember no more.

I opened my eyes in daylight. My head was roughly bandaged, and the man with the withered arm was watching my face. I looked about me, trying to remember what had happened, and for a space I could not recollect. I turned to the corner, and saw the old woman, no longer **abstracted**, pouring out some drops of medicine from a little blue phial into a glass. 'Where am I?' I asked. 'I seem to remember you, and yet I cannot remember who you are.'

They told me then, and I heard of the haunted Red Room as one who hears a tale. 'We found you at dawn,' said he, 'and there was blood on your forehead and lips.'

---

incontinently: immediately
abstracted: withdrawn

It was very slowly I recovered my memory of my experience. 'You believe now,' said the old man, 'that the room is haunted?' He spoke no longer as one who greets an intruder, but as one who grieves for a broken friend.

'Yes,' said I; 'the room is haunted.'

'And you have seen it. And we, who have lived here all our lives, have never set eyes upon it. Because we have never dared . . . Tell us, is it truly the old earl who' –

'No,' said I; 'it is not.'

'I told you so,' said the old lady, with the glass in her hand. 'It is his poor young countess who was frightened' –

'It is not,' I said. 'There is neither ghost of earl nor ghost of countess in that room, there is no ghost there at all; but worse, far worse' –

'Well?' they said.

'The worst of all the things that haunt poor mortal man,' said I; 'and that is, in all its nakedness – *Fear*! Fear that will not have light or sound, that will not bear with reason, that deafens and darkens and overwhelms. It followed me through the corridor, it fought against me in the room' –

I stopped abruptly. There was an interval of silence. My hand went up to my bandages.

Then the man with the shade sighed and spoke. 'That is it,' said he. 'I knew that was it. A Power of Darkness. To put such a curse upon a woman! It lurks there always. You can feel it even in the daytime, even of a bright summer's day, in the hangings, in the curtains, keeping behind you however you face about. In the dusk it creeps along the corridor and follows you, so that you dare not turn. There is Fear in that room of hers – black Fear, and there will be – so long as this house of sin endures.'

Non-fiction passages linked to *The Red Room* (1896)

England's haunted houses

In Lorraine Castle, the narrator is haunted not by a ghost but by Fear. Some of England's haunted houses fill people with terror. Others seem to have ghosts that are more friendly than frightening. The true 'ghost reports' that follow may help you to make up your own minds on the subject.

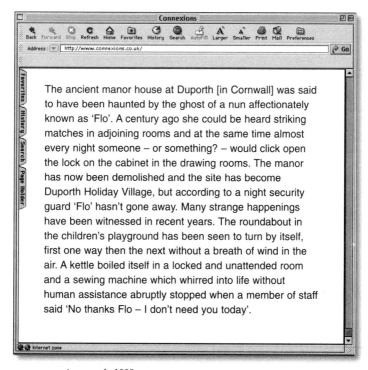

The ancient manor house at Duporth [in Cornwall] was said to have been haunted by the ghost of a nun affectionately known as 'Flo'. A century ago she could be heard striking matches in adjoining rooms and at the same time almost every night someone – or something? – would click open the lock on the cabinet in the drawing rooms. The manor has now been demolished and the site has become Duporth Holiday Village, but according to a night security guard 'Flo' hasn't gone away. Many strange happenings have been witnessed in recent years. The roundabout in the children's playground has been seen to turn by itself, first one way then the next without a breath of wind in the air. A kettle boiled itself in a locked and unattended room and a sewing machine which whirred into life without human assistance abruptly stopped when a member of staff said 'No thanks Flo – I don't need you today'.

www.connexions.co.uk, 1999

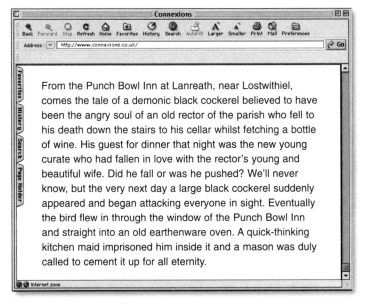

From the Punch Bowl Inn at Lanreath, near Lostwithiel, comes the tale of a demonic black cockerel believed to have been the angry soul of an old rector of the parish who fell to his death down the stairs to his cellar whilst fetching a bottle of wine. His guest for dinner that night was the new young curate who had fallen in love with the rector's young and beautiful wife. Did he fall or was he pushed? We'll never know, but the very next day a large black cockerel suddenly appeared and began attacking everyone in sight. Eventually the bird flew in through the window of the Punch Bowl Inn and straight into an old earthenware oven. A quick-thinking kitchen maid imprisoned him inside it and a mason was duly called to cement it up for all eternity.

www.connexions.co.uk, 1999

There is a ghostly old man at Kensington Palace, London. People who live and work there often see him. He looks worried and he sits at a window staring out. He watches a weathercock on the roof and mutters 'Why don't they come?' Nobody is frightened of him because he doesn't bother anyone. He usually vanishes after a few seconds.

This is the ghost of King George II. He was the King of Britain from 1727 to 1760. In October 1760 George was staying at Kensington Palace. He was ill and waiting for some important news by ship from Germany. There was a strong westerly wind so no ships could enter the British harbour. Every day, George stared at the weathercock hoping the wind would change. Sadly, he died before the news arrived. Now his ghost sits waiting for the news.

Rupert Matthews, 1997

At Borley Rectory [in Suffolk] witnesses reported a ghostly nun wandering the grounds, keys falling from locks before vanishing, disconnected bells ringing, and the discovery of a skull. In the 1930s, investigators claimed contact with unhappy spirits, one of them a nun who had been strangled and buried in the grounds. The spirits warned that a terrible fire would destroy the rectory, revealing buried bodies. Within a year, a fire did destroy the house and human remains were found.

Ivor Baddiel and Tracey Blezard, 1998

Activities and assignments
Cluster 1

The Poor Relation's Story
by Charles Dickens

1 **a** What do you understand by the phrase 'a castle in the air'?

At the end of the story, Michael, the poor relation, tells his family: 'My Castle is in the Air!' (page 13). Why does this make us reconsider the account he has given them of his life?

b Make a chart like the one below, comparing Michael's life as it *really* is with the way he describes it to his relatives.

	Truth	Fiction
His home life		
His employment		
His financial circumstances		
His wife and children		
His social life		

2 Re-read the part of the story where Michael is disowned by Uncle Chill (pages 6 to 9), from 'As I came downstairs next morning' to 'He snarled at me as I went out, and I never saw him again'.

a Find evidence from the text that Uncle Chill is:

- miserly
- heartless
- self-centred
- driven by greed for money.

b What methods does the author use to present Uncle Chill as a thoroughly unpleasant character? Think about:

- his name, and the name of his female servant

- the descriptions of his house: how do these reflect Uncle Chill himself?

- the language and tone of voice Uncle Chill uses to Michael

- the language and tone of voice Uncle Chill uses to Christiana and her mother.

3 Re-read the part of the story where Michael describes his relationship with John Spatter, his business partner and schoolboy friend (pages 10 to 12).

   a How does the author make us feel sorry for Michael here? Think about:

- how John is shown to take advantage of Michael's trusting nature

- the author's use of irony. (Remember that Michael's account of this conversation is the exact opposite of what was actually said.)

   b By this stage in the story, what pattern has emerged in the way Michael is treated by his relatives and friends, including his fiancée Christiana?

4 Michael's friendship with Little Frank is of great importance to him.

   a With a partner, look at the statements that follow. Decide which of them give a true impression of the friendship. Are any of them false? Use the evidence of the whole story to decide.

- Frank is Michael's only friend.

- Michael plans to turn Frank against the relatives who have wronged him in order to get his revenge.

- Frank acts as a substitute child for Michael.

- Frank is like Michael in character.

- Michael can only make relationships with children since he is childlike himself.

b Re-read the closing paragraphs of the story, starting at 'I am not (said the poor relation, looking at the fire . . .)' (page 12).

In this section, Michael paints 'quite a picture of Home'. Which words and phrases convey his idea of 'Home' most strongly?

By ending the story in this way, what feelings towards Michael and his relatives does the author leave you with?

5 Read the non-fiction passages on pages 14 to 16. With a partner, or in a group, talk about the following.

- The impressions they give of poverty in mid-nineteenth century London.

- Your own response to them.

- The light they shed on this story.

You could present this as a GCSE Speaking and Listening assignment.

6 *The Poor Relation's Story* is about a man driven into poverty by his family and friends.

Thinking over your responses to the story, note down the main ways in which the author makes us feel:

- sympathetic to Michael

- critical of those who cause his downfall.

On pages 14 to 16 there are non-fiction passages to help you place this story in its social, cultural and historical context.

The Half-Brothers
by Elizabeth Gaskell

1   In the early part of the story, the author presents Helen, the boys' mother, as a tragic figure.

   a   Look carefully at the following points in the text. In each case, say how the author's descriptions arouse pity for Helen.

- The deaths of her first husband and her young daughter.

- Her reaction to William's offer of marriage.

- Her reaction to William's feelings about Gregory.

- The scene of her death.

   b   Helen marries William although 'she did not love him' (page 20). Suggest three reasons why she agrees to re-marry. Quote from the text to back up your ideas.

    Then read the non-fiction passages on pages 30 to 32. How do they increase your understanding of Helen's decision to re-marry?

2   As he grows up, the narrator is favoured. Gregory, on the other hand, is treated as inferior.

   a   Make a chart like the one below, to show the differences between Gregory's upbringing and his half-brother's. Draw your material from pages 22 to 24.

The narrator	Gregory
1 Seen as the 'young master' – treated with respect.	1 Seen as an 'orphan' – treated as 'lumpish and loutish'.
2 Gets 'plenty of praise' at school – trained up to inherit the farm.	2 Suffers 'scolding and flogging' at school – trained up to be 'a kind of shepherd'.

Make three further entries on your chart. Include words and phrases from the text.

b What purpose do you think the author has in bringing out these differences so strongly? Think of the story as a whole, especially the incident on the fells and William's grief at the end.

3 Re-read the three paragraphs describing how the narrator gets lost and almost dies on the fells, from 'Off I set at a pretty quick pace' to ' . . . dulled as the sound might be by the thickened air (pages 24 to 26).

In this episode, how does the author create the feeling that the narrator is about to meet a tragic death? Think about her use of:

- first-person voice and viewpoint

- details of the setting

- language and sentence structure.

4 Re-read the part of the story where Gregory saves his half-brother and dies as a result (pages 26 to 28).

a Note down quotations from the text to illustrate each of the following qualities in Gregory's character:

- courage
- loyalty
- unselfishness
- love.

b Looking over the story as a whole:

- *compare* these qualities with those shown by Helen

- *contrast* these qualities with those shown by the narrator.

5 'My father's last words were, "God forgive me my hardness of heart towards the fatherless child!" ' (page 29).

a Put William in the 'hot seat'. Question him about:

- his feelings towards Helen
- his reaction to Helen's death
- his treatment of Gregory
- his favouritism towards his own son
- his feelings about Gregory's death
- his instructions for burial.

You could present this as a GCSE Speaking and Listening assignment.

b Do you think the author means us to see William as simply cruel and heartless, or as a man for whom we ought to feel some sympathy? Support your opinion with quotations from the text.

6 *The Half-Brothers* is the story of a family tragedy.

Thinking over your responses to the story, note down the main reasons why this tragedy occurs.

On pages 30 to 32 there are non-fiction passages to help you place this story in its social, cultural and historical context.

The Parvenue
by Mary Shelley

1 Fanny, the narrator, says 'How happy my childhood was!' (page 34).

The reasons she gives for this include:

- living in the countryside

- being close to Susan, her twin sister

- living as part of a large family of half-brothers and half-sisters

- enjoying her mother's companionship and love

- helping poor people.

Find quotations from the opening pages of the story to illustrate each of these points.

2 Re-read the part of the story describing Fanny's wedding and the two years she and Lord Reginald spend abroad. Begin on page 36 at 'My wedding day came' and stop on page 38 at 'Was I right?'

a Note down the main reasons why, during this time, 'many things pained me' (page 37).

b Lord Reginald disapproves of Fanny's behaviour while they are abroad, to the extent that she says 'I lost my husband's affections' (page 38).

Why does their relationship become so strained? To help you decide:

- re-read pages 39 to 42

- read through the non-fiction passages on pages 43 and 44 about the role of a wife in Victorian times.

3 On her return to England, Fanny finds that 'all [my family] depended on me' (page 39).

   a Make a chart like the one below, showing how Fanny's relatives come to rely on the money she has acquired through marriage.

Members of Fanny's family	What they need, and why
Her father	Needs more capital to prevent a business venture from failing.
Her half-brothers and half-sisters	
Susan	
Her mother	
Her brother-in-law, Lawrence Cooper	

   b Re-read the paragraph on page 40 beginning 'Oh, what thick clouds now obscured my destiny!'

     How do the style and language of this paragraph **i** convey Fanny's feelings of misery, and **ii** contrast with the earlier descriptions of her idyllic childhood?

4 'Choose between us – you never see them [your family] more, or we part for ever' (page 42).

  Faced with this choice, Fanny's decision is to separate from Lord Reginald. The marriage is over.

   a Put Fanny in the 'hot seat'. Question her about:

- what influenced her decision the most
- whether it made her life happier
- whether she regrets marrying Lord Reginald
- who, or what, she blames for the breakdown of her marriage.

You could present this as a GCSE Speaking and Listening assignment.

b In Fanny's position, would *you* have made the same decision about ending your marriage to look after your family? To help you decide, read the non-fiction passages on pages 45 and 46 about separation and divorce in the nineteenth century.

5 *The Parvenue* is the story of a woman who becomes deeply unhappy because her marriage fails.

Thinking over your responses to the story, note down what the author is saying about marriage between people from different classes in Victorian times.

On pages 43 to 46 there are non-fiction passages to help you place this story in its social, cultural and historical context.

To Please His Wife
by Thomas Hardy

1   By the end of Chapter one, Shadrach Jolliffe and Joanna agree to marry. Yet neither loves the other.

    a Each has different reasons for marrying. Basing your comments on the extracts below, say what these differences are.

        Joanna

- 'Joanna contrived to wean him away from her gentler and younger rival' (page 49).

- 'Joanna was not altogether satisfied with the sailor. She liked his attentions, and she coveted the dignity of matrimony; but she had never been deeply in love with Joliffe' (page 50).

- 'Green envy had overspread Joanna at the scene' (page 52).

        Shadrach

- 'I have the best of feelings for Joanna, but I know that from the beginning she hasn't cared for me more than in a friendly way' (page 51).

- ' "It is all the same as before," he answered, "if you say it must be" ' (page 53).

- 'Shadrach was a religious and scrupulous man, who respected his word as his life' (page 53).

    b In Chapter one, which of the two characters – Shadrach or Joanna – would you say the author wants us to sympathise with more? How does he guide our response to them?

2   In Chapter two, Joanna's fortunes change for the worse while Emily's change for the better.

    a Make a flow-diagram showing how and why the financial/social gap between the two women grows wider.

Joanna's fortunes	Emily's fortunes
1 Her mother dies: she and Shadrach start running a small grocer's shop, but it does not prosper.	1 She marries a wealthy merchant: she moves to a rich, fashionable house and has no need to work.
↓	↓
2	2

b How does Emily's growing wealth affect:

- Joanna's feelings about her family's social position

- Joanna's attitude towards Shadrach

- Joanna and Shadrach's relationship as man and wife?

Find evidence from pages 54 to 60 of the text to back up your ideas.

3 At the end of Chapter two, Shadrach agrees to a second sea voyage, this time with his sons.

Act out the conversation in which Joanna and Shadrach discuss whether a second voyage should be made. Prepare for this by:

i re-reading pages 59 and 60 of the story

ii reading the non-fiction passages printed on pages 66 and 67.

Bring out the reasons for and against the decision. Include some of your own views as well as those given in the story.

You could present this as a GCSE Speaking and Listening assignment.

4   On page 64, the author describes Joanna as a 'grief-stricken soul'.

Divide your class into two groups. Both groups should examine chapter three carefully: **Group A** to find evidence that the author wants us to feel pity for Joanna, and **Group B** to find evidence that he wants us to feel her sufferings are fully deserved.

Use the following extracts to start building up your case. Then argue it out in class.

- ' "Ah, will they come? The doubt is more than a woman can bear" ' (page 62).

- 'She had always feared and detested the sea; to her it was a treacherous, restless, slimy creature, glorying in the griefs of women' (page 62).

- 'The fancy grew almost to an hallucination: she could never turn her worn eyes to the step without seeing them there' (page 63).

- 'This was her purgation for the sin of making them the slaves of her ambition' (page 63).

- ' "What can you want with a bereaved crone like me! . . . You wish to separate me and mine!" ' (page 64).

- 'Her hair greyed and whitened, deep lines channeled her forehead, and her form grew gaunt and stooping' (page 64).

- ' "O, Mrs Jolliffe, I didn't know it was you," said the young man kindly, for he was aware how her baseless expectations moved her. "No; nobody has come" ' (page 65).

5   *To Please His Wife* is a story about how lack of money, combined with social ambition, can destroy a marriage.

Thinking over your responses to the story, note down the main ways in which the author presents this theme to us.

On pages 66 to 69 there are non-fiction passages to help you place this story in its social, cultural and historical context.

The Adventure of the Beryl Coronet
by Arthur Conan Doyle

1   Work with a partner. Take turns to put yourself in Sherlock Holmes's place. Your partner should act as a journalist and interview you about how you solved the crime described in this story. Give detailed answers to the following questions.

- *Even before you visited Mr Holder's house, Fairbank, you were sure that Arthur was not the criminal. Why?*

- *When you went down to Fairbank, your first action was to examine the stable lane. What were you looking for? Did you find it?*

- *Why did you disguise yourself as a vagabond, make friends with Sir George Burnwell's manservant and then return secretly to Fairbank?*

- *Were you surprised when Mr Holder brought you the news that Mary, his niece, had taken flight?*

- *How did you manage to recover the stolen beryls?*

The interviewer should ask supplementary questions to bring out **i** the full truth about the crime, and **ii** Holmes's attitude towards the story's main characters: Arthur, Mr Holder and Mary.

You could present this as a GCSE Speaking and Listening assignment.

2   When Mr Holder sees Arthur with the beryls, he says 'You have dishonoured me forever!' (page 78). After hearing the truth, he says: 'How cruelly I have misjudged him!' (page 92).

   a What leads Mr Holder to believe, wrongly, that Arthur has 'dishonoured' his family by stealing the jewels? Base your answer on the following passages.

- 'He has been a disappointment to me, Mr Holmes – a grievous disappointment' (page 75).

- 'He learned to play heavily at cards and to squander money on the turf' (page 75).

- ' "Look here, dad," said he with his eyes cast down, "can you let me have £200?" ' (page 77).

- ' "You blackguard!" I shouted, beside myself with rage. "You have destroyed it! . . . Where are the jewels which you have stolen?" ' (page 78).

- 'My God, what shall I do! I have lost my honour, my gems, and my son in one night!' (page 80).

b Use the passages below to show how Arthur acts in a way that actually *protects* his family's 'honour'.

- ' "Keep your forgiveness for those who ask for it," he answered, turning away from me with a sneer' (page 80).

- ' "Why is he silent, then, if he is innocent?" ' (page 83).

- ' "You owe a very humble apology to that noble lad, your son" ' (page 89).

- 'As long as she was on the scene he could not take any action without a horrible exposure of the woman whom he loved' (page 91).

- 'the lad could not say a word without compromising his own family' (page 94).

3 Consider the following statements about Mary.

- Mr Holder's view of her as 'sweet' and 'loving' is quite wrong.

- She is happy to let Arthur take the blame for her own crime.

- She is a skilful deceiver.

- She is the innocent victim of Sir George Burnwell's greed for money.

- She, not Arthur, brings dishonour to the family.

Which of these are true and which are false? Back up your opinion by noting down at least one quotation relevant to each statement.

4 **a** Re-read the beginning of the story, as far as ' "Pray compose yourself, sir," said Holmes' (page 71).

What methods does the author use here to make us feel sympathy for Mr Holder? Think about:

- particular phrases describing his appearance and actions

- the use of Dr Watson's point of view.

- Holmes's tone and language when speaking to Mr Holder.

b Re-read the ending of the story, from 'I will tell you then, what occurred in your house last night' (page 90).

What methods does the author use here to make us feel sympathy for Arthur? Think about:

- the use of delayed information

- Holmes's language when describing Arthur

- Mr Holder's reactions to hearing the truth about his son.

5 *The Adventure of the Beryl Coronet* shows how money and social reputation can divide a family.

Thinking over your responses to the story, note down the main ways in which the author explores this theme.

On pages 96 to 98 there are non-fiction passages to help you place this story in its social, cultural and historical context.

Coursework assignments on Cluster 1

Assignment 1

The stories in Cluster 1 explore conflict within the family.

How do their authors show that family conflicts are caused by:

- marriage
- wealth and poverty
- social status and social reputation?

Write mainly about **three** stories.

Assignment 2

These stories describe individuals who are the victims of nineteenth-century social attitudes and values.

How do their authors:

- present the individuals as victim-figures
- arouse the reader's sympathy for them?

Write mainly about **three** characters from different stories.

Activities and assignments
Cluster 2

The Superstitious Man's Story
by Thomas Hardy

1 'There was something very strange about William's death
   – very strange indeed!' (page 100).

   In this story, four characters have very strange
   experiences connected with William's death:

   • Betty Privett [William's wife]

   • Nancy Weedle

   • John Chiles

   • Philip Hookhorn.

   On a chart like the one below, note down in your own
   words what these experiences are. Fill in a different
   column for each character.

Strange experiences			
Betty	Nancy	John	Philip

2 a Create an 'interview panel' made up of Betty, Nancy,
      John and Philip.

      Other members of your class or group should question
      them in detail, asking them to:

      • *describe* what they know about William's death

      • provide their own *explanation* for what happened.

b Read the non-fiction passage on pages 104 and 105.

Then do your own research into other superstitions surrounding death. You will find material in books of legends, in local histories, on Internet websites and so on.

Having prepared carefully, make a presentation on this subject to your class or group. You could present **a** and/or **b** as a GCSE Speaking and Listening assignment.

3 This story is structured in episodes, like a TV serial. The longest episode is the first, running from the start to '. . . and went to bed herself' (page 101).

a How many further episodes can you find? How does the narrator signal the beginning of each new episode?

b Show how each episode you have identified adds a further layer of superstition to the one(s) before it.

What does the author achieve by building up the story in this way?

4 The story's narrator is an old countryman. The story he tells has a distinctive style.

a Look carefully at the following extracts.

- 'William, as you may know, was a curious, silent man' (page 100)

- 'the sexton, who told me o't, said he'd not known the bell go so heavy in his hand in years' (page 100).

- '*Mind and do the door*' (page 101).

- ' "Old Midsummer yesterday, was it? Faith I didn't think whe'r 'twas Midsummer or Michaelmas" ' (page 102).

- 'and as he looked towards his fellow-mower he saw one of those great white miller's-souls as we call 'em – that is to say, a miller-moth – come from William's open mouth' (page 102).

In these examples, how does the author give the impression that the story is being spoken? Think about his use of:

- the first-person voice
- a conversational style and tone
- non-standard English and regional dialect.

b Why do you think the author chooses a 'spoken style' for this story? Does it suit the subject matter?

5 *The Superstitious Man's Story* shows how the supernatural can play an important part in ordinary people's lives.

Thinking over your responses to the story, note down the main ways in which the author weaves together the ordinary and the extraordinary.

On pages 104 and 105 there are non-fiction passages to help you place this story in its social, cultural and historical context.

The Trial for Murder
by Charles Dickens

1   In this story the ghost of a murdered man influences all the main events, including the trial of the man who killed him.

   a Make a chart like the one below to show **i** what actions the ghost performs, and **ii** their effect on the narrator [the banker] and on other characters.

Ghost's action	Effect
1 Produces a picture in the banker's mind of the room in which he was murdered.	Makes the banker 'see' the place where he was killed – proves it really happened.
2 Appears walking down Piccadilly following his murderer.	Fixes both their faces in the banker's mind – shows that he wants revenge.

   Aim to make up to ten entries on your chart.

   b Compare your completed chart with a partner's. Take turns to explain what you have written, backing up your points with quotations from the text.

   You could present this as a GCSE Speaking and Listening assignment.

2   **a** Find evidence that, as the trial goes on, the ghost's appearances become **i** more frequent, and **ii** more influential. Think about:

   • the ways in which the ghost behaves in the courtroom

   • the ways in which others apart from the banker are physically affected by the ghost – for instance, Mr Harker, the defence counsel, a female witness, the Judge.

b Why do you think the author establishes this pattern within the story? How does it help to build up a strong sense of the supernatural?

3 The story's main setting, the Court-House, is carefully conveyed.

    a Look closely at the following descriptions of this setting.

- 'There was a dense brown fog in Piccadilly, and it became positively black and in the last degree oppressive East of Temple Bar' (page 110).

- 'I found the passages and staircases of the Court-House flaringly lighted with gas, and the Court itself similarly illuminated' (page 110).

- 'I looked about the Court as well as I could through the cloud of fog and breath that was heavy in it. I noticed a black vapour hanging like a murky curtain outside the great windows' (page 110).

- 'the same lights kindled at the same hour when there had been any natural light of day, the same foggy curtain outside the great windows when it was foggy' (page 116).

What impressions does the author give here of the atmosphere in and around the Court-House? Think about **i** the dominant colours, **ii** references to the light, and **iii** images of clouds and curtains.

    b Look closely at this description of the ghost as the banker delivers the Jury's verdict.

- 'As I took my place, his eyes rested on me with great attention; he seemed satisfied, and slowly shook a great grey veil, which he carried on his arm for the first time, over his head and whole form. As I gave in our verdict, 'Guilty', the veil collapsed, all was gone, and his place was empty' (page 116).

What links are there here with the descriptions
in **a** above?

What is the author's purpose in drawing our attention
to them?

4   Re-read the story's final paragraph (page 117).

The condemned man claims to have been haunted too.
By whom? When?

Do you think this ending fits in with the pattern of the
rest of the story, or is it an extra 'twist' that leaves the
reader confused? Give reasons for your view.

5   *The Trial for Murder* is the story of a ghost who seeks
justice for himself from beyond the grave.

Thinking over your responses to the story, note down the
main ways in which the author conveys this theme to us.

*On pages 118 to 120 there are non-fiction passages to
help you place this story in its social, cultural and
historical context.*

The Ostler
by Wilkie Collins

1 Look carefully at the opening paragraphs of the story, down to 'There's the queerest story – of a dreadful kind, too, mind you – connected with him and his dream, that was ever told' (pages 121 and 122).

  a How does the author arouse our curiosity here about Isaac's 'dreadful' story? Think about:

  • the descriptions of Isaac's appearance in paragraph one

  • what Isaac says while talking in his sleep

  • the use of a first-person viewpoint (the narrator's)

  • the use of the present tense

  • the use of broken sentences.

  b The setting, a stable at an inn, is ordinary and down-to-earth. Why do you think the author chooses to begin a story full of extraordinary events in such a setting?

2 Re-read the part of the story where Isaac is visited by 'the dream woman'. Start from 'It was half-past eleven by the clock in the passage' (page 125) and stop at 'The fair woman with the knife was gone' (page 127).

  a How does the author create a feeling of **i** suspense, and **ii** terror in this section? Base your analysis on the following extracts.

  • 'The bleak autumn wind was still blowing, and the solemn, monotonous, surging moan of it in the wood was dreary and awful to hear through the night-silence' (page 125).

  • 'Speechless, with no expression in her face, with no noise following her footfall – she came closer and closer – stopped – and slowly raised the knife' (page 126).

- 'The flame diminished to a little blue point, and the room grew dark. A moment, or less, if possible, passed so – and then the wick flamed up, smokily, for the last time' (page 127).

b Make a chart like the one below to show how the dream woman's appearance and actions mirror Rebecca's, later in the story.

The dream woman	Rebecca
1 Dream woman has fair hair, light grey eyes and a droop in the left eyelid. 2	Rebecca's appearance is identical to the dream woman's.

Make three more entries on your chart.

What other examples can you find in the story of coincidence or 'foretelling'? What do you think the author achieves by creating these patterns?

3 'What was the fair woman with the knife? The creature of a dream, or that other creature from the unknown world called among men by the name of ghost?' (page 129).

Work with a partner or in a group. Look over the whole story and decide on your answer to the above question. Take particular account of:

- the change in Isaac's character after he meets Rebecca

- the 'superstitious dread' of Isaac's mother

- Rebecca's disappearance at the end of the story

- the non-fiction passages on pages 145 to 147.

Present your findings to the class, backing up what you say with quotations from the text.

You could present this as a GCSE Speaking and Listening assignment.

4 Re-read the ending of the story, from 'At this point in the narrative the landlord paused' (page 144).

    a For what reason does Isaac continue to live in fear and torment? Why is this greatest at **i** a certain time of night, and **ii** a certain time of year?

    b How does the story's ending maintain the sense of mystery that the author has built up all the way through? Think about:

- what the landlord says concerning his own knowledge of Isaac

- the way the story returns to where it began

- the way the author leaves the story open-ended: ' " Who can tell!" said I.'

5 *The Ostler* is a mystery story in which suspense and terror both play an important part.

Choose **three** different episodes from the story. Thinking over your responses to them, note down the main ways in which the author creates a feeling of suspense and terror.

On pages 145 to 147 there are non-fiction passages to help you place this story in its social, cultural and historical context.

Confession Found in a Prison
by Charles Dickens

1   In the first half of this story, the narrator plans and carries out his young nephew's murder.

Divide your class into two groups.

Group A looks for evidence that the narrator planned the murder in a *rational* frame of mind and had clear motives for it. (These might include greed for money, jealousy and revenge.)

Group B looks for evidence that the narrator was driven to commit the murder by forces beyond his control – and that he went about it in an *irrational* frame of mind.

Present your evidence. Back it up with quotations from pages 148 to 150 of the text.

You could present this as a GCSE Speaking and Listening assignment.

2   Re-read the account of the murder, from 'Hard by our cottage' (page 150) to 'with his cheek resting upon his little hand' (page 151).

How do the following extracts make us feel pity for the young boy and horror at his murder? Think about the author's **i** choice of language, **ii** use of contrast, and **iii** construction of sentences.

- 'I was sure that I had him in my net for I had heard him from prattling of the toy' (page 150).

- 'on the third day he passed me, running joyously along, with his silken hair streaming in the wind and he singing – God have mercy upon me! – singing a merry ballad – who could hardly lisp the words' (page 151).

- 'I, a full-grown man, tracked the footsteps of that baby as he approached the water's brink' (page 151).

- 'and he lying at my feet stark dead – dabbled here and there with blood but otherwise no different from what I had seen him in his sleep – in the same attitude too, with his cheek resting upon his little hand' (page 151).

3 After committing the murder, the narrator lives in a constant state of fear and torment.

   a Copy and complete a chart like the one below, to show how the narrator's attempts to hide the crime do not relieve this torment.

Narrator's actions	Narrator still tormented: quotations
1 Hides the body in a thicket.	'there was a glow-worm like the visible spirit of God upon the murdered child' (page 152).
2 Buries the body in a shallow grave.	'visions of the plot of grass, through which now a hand and now a foot and now the head itself was starting out' (page 152).

Make two further entries on this chart.

   b Look carefully at the quotations on your chart. What does the language suggest about the reasons for the narrator's torment? How far does it stem from his fear of discovery, and how far from his horror at what he has done?

4 This story is told through a 'flashback' technique.

   a Re-read paragraph two (page 148), then the final paragraph (page 155). What purpose do you think the author has in beginning and ending his story in the present?

  b What feelings about the narrator does the final
  paragraph leave you with? Think about:

- the quote 'That I fell upon my knees . . . and
  prayed to be forgiven' (page 155)

- the quote 'That I am alone in this stone dungeon
  with my evil spirit' (page 155)

- the use of first-person voice and viewpoint

- the repetition of specific sentence structures.

5 *Confession Found in a Prison* is the story of a man
  possessed by the forces of evil.

  Thinking over your responses to the story, note down the
  main ways in which the author builds up a sense of evil
  throughout the narrative.

*On pages 156 and 157 there are non-fiction passages to
help you place this story in its social, cultural and
historical context.*

The Red Room
by H. G. Wells

1 In the course of the story, we are given glimpses into the 'ghostly tradition' of the Red Room at Lorraine Castle.

   a Make a chart like the one below, showing what we find out about the history of the Red Room.

Information	Evidence
A previous owner of the Castle died in the Red Room.	'. . .the great red room of Lorraine Castle, in which the young duke had died' (page 162).
A previous owner's wife had a curse put on her and is said to haunt the Red Room.	

   Add two or three more entries to your chart.

   b Why do you think the author gives only *hints* about the Red Room's history, rather than revealing the full story?

2 At the start of the story the narrator meets three old servants who take care of Lorraine Castle.

   Look carefully at **i** how they are described, and **ii** how they react to the narrator's boast 'it will take a very tangible ghost to frighten me' (page 158). Use the following extracts as reference-points.

   • ' "It is your own choosing," said the man with the withered arm, and glanced at me askance' (page 158).

   • ' "There's a many things to see, when one's still but eight-and-twenty" ' (page 158).

   • 'He supported himself by a single crutch, his eyes were covered by a shade, and his lower lip, half-averted, hung pale and pink from his decaying yellow teeth' (page 158).

- 'their gaunt silences, their bent carriage, their evident unfriendliness to me and to one another' (page 159).

- ' "This night of all nights!" said the old woman)' (page 160).

What impressions do these descriptions give of the old servants?

Why do you think the author chooses to begin the story with them?

3 **a** 'I shut them in and walked down the chilly, echoing passage' (page 160).

   Pick out three descriptions from the narrator's journey down the passage to the Red Room that create a mood of **i** suspense, and **ii** growing tension. Say as precisely as you can *how* they do so.

   b Re-read the account of what happens to the narrator in the Red Room, from 'Even with that, however, the brooding expectation of the vigil weighed heavily upon me' (page 164) to 'and then I remember no more' (page 166).

   Pick out four passages that show the narrator is fighting a losing battle against what is later described as 'A Power of Darkness' (page 167). How do the passages convey an impression of the narrator's mounting terror? Think about:

   - how the narrator increasingly loses control

   - how the objects in the room seem to take on a life of their own

   - how the first-person viewpoint helps us to share the narrator's experiences and feelings

   - the author's choice of **i** verbs, and **ii** adjectives

   - the length and structure of sentences.

4 Compare the ending of the story from 'I opened my eyes in daylight' (page 166), with its opening three pages (pages 158 to 160).

    a How has the narrator changed? Think about:

- his physical appearance

- the way he speaks to the old servants, and they to him

- his attitude towards the Red Room.

What points is the author making by showing us these changes?

    b By the end of the story, the narrator believes 'the room is haunted'; he also says, 'there is no ghost there at all' (page 167).

What do you think the author means us to conclude from this?

5 *The Red Room* is a story about 'The worst of all the things that haunt poor mortal man . . . *Fear!*' (page 167).

Thinking over your responses to the story, note down the main ways in which the author builds up a strong feeling of fear throughout the narrative.

On pages 168 to 170 there are non-fiction passages to help you place this story in its social, cultural and historical context.

Coursework assignments on Cluster 2

Assignment 1

These stories describe strange and supernatural events.

How do their authors create a feeling of:

- the extraordinary
- fear and terror
- suspense?

Write mainly about **three** stories.

Assignment 2

These stories describe individuals at the mercy of forces beyond their control.

Choose **three** such characters from different stories. Compare their experiences.

How do the authors make these experiences seem strange and frightening to the reader?

Founding Editors: Anne and Ian Serraillier

Chinua Achebe Things Fall Apart
David Almond Skellig
Maya Angelou I Know Why the Caged Bird Sings
Margaret Atwood The Handmaid's Tale
Jane Austen Pride and Prejudice
Stan Barstow Joby: A Kind of Loving
Nina Bawden Carrie's War; The Finding; Humbug
Malorie Blackman Tell Me No Lies; Words Last Forever
Charlotte Brontë Jane Eyre
Emily Brontë Wuthering Heights
Melvin Burgess and Lee Hall Billy Elliot
Betsy Byars The Midnight Fox; The Pinballs; The Eighteenth Emergency
Victor Canning The Runaways
Sir Arthur Conan Doyle Sherlock Holmes Short Stories
Susan Cooper King of Shadows
Robert Cormier Heroes
Roald Dahl Danny; The Champion of the World; The Wonderful Story of Henry Sugar; George's Marvellous Medicine; The Witches; Boy; Going Solo; Matilda; My Year
Anita Desai The Village by the Sea
Charles Dickens A Christmas Carol; Great Expectations; A Charles Dickens Selection
Berlie Doherty Granny was a Buffer Girl; Street Child
Roddy Doyle Paddy Clarke Ha Ha Ha
George Eliot Silas Marner
Anne Fine The Granny Project
Leon Garfield Six Shakespeare Stories
Ann Halam Dr Franklin's Island
Thomas Hardy The Withered Arm and Other Wessex Tales; The Mayor of Casterbridge
Ernest Hemmingway The Old Man and the Sea; A Farewell to Arms
Barry Hines A Kestrel For A Knave
Nigel Hinton Buddy; Buddy's Song
Anne Holm I Am David

Janni Howker Badger on the Barge; The Nature of the Beast;
Martin Farrell
Pete Johnson The Protectors
Geraldine Kaye Comfort Herself
Daniel Keyes Flowers for Algernon
Dick King-Smith The Sheep-Pig
Elizabeth Laird Red Sky in the Morning
D H Lawrence The Fox and The Virgin and the Gypsy; Selected Tales
Harper Lee To Kill a Mockingbird
C Day Lewis The Otterbury Incident
Joan Linguard Across the Barricades
Penelope Lively The Ghost of Thomas Kemp
Geraldine McCaughrean Stories from Shakespeare; Pack of Lies
Bernard MacLaverty Cal; The Best of Bernard MacLaverty
Jan Mark Heathrow Nights
James Vance Marshall Walkabout
Ian McEwan The Daydreamer; A Child in Time
Michael Morpurgo The Wreck of the Zanzibar; Why the Whales Came;
Arthur, High King of Britain; Kensuke's Kingdom; From Hereabout Hill;
Robin of Sherwood
Beverley Naidoo No Turning Back; The Other Side of Truth
Bill Naughton The Goalkeeper's Revenge
New Windmill A Charles Dickens Selection
New Windmill Anthology of Challenging Texts: Thoughtlines
New Windmill Book of Classic Short Stories
New Windmill Book of Fiction and Non-fiction: Taking Off!
New Windmill Book of Greek Myths
New Windmill Book of Haunting Tales
New Windmill Book of Humorous Stories: Don't Make Me Laugh
New Windmill Book of Nineteenth Century Short Stories
New Windmill Book of Non-fiction: Get Real
New Windmill Book of Non-fiction: Real Lives, Real Times
New Windmill Book of Scottish Short Stories
New Windmill Book of Short Stories: Fast and Curious
New Windmill Book of Short Stories: From Beginning to End
New Windmill Book of Short Stories: Into the Unknown
New Windmill Book of Short Stories: Tales with a Twist
New Windmill Book of Short Stories: Trouble in Two Centuries
New Windmill Book of Short Stories: Ways with Words
New Windmill Book of Stories from Many Cultures and Traditions;
Fifty-Fifty Tuti-Fruity Chocolate Chip

How many have you read?